CALIFORNIA MIDDLE SCHOOL

Mathematics
Concepts and Skills
COURSE 2

Larson   Boswell   Kanold   Stiff

Practice Workbook

The Practice Workbook includes additional practice
and problem solving exercises for each lesson of
every chapter.

McDougal Littell
A HOUGHTON MIFFLIN COMPANY
Evanston, Illinois • Boston • Dallas

ISBN-13: 978-0-618-07832-5   ISBN-10: 0-618-07832-0

17 18 19 20–VEI–09 08 07

Contents

The table gives the box-office gross income in millions of five movies.

Movie	Box-office Gross
A	$191.6
B	$184.0
C	$172.0
D	$141.6
E	$108.3

1. Which movie earned 141.6 million dollars?

2. How much more money did Movie B earn than Movie E?

3. What were the total earnings for Movies A and D?

The bar graph at the right shows university champions in wrestling from 1970–1996, and the number of times each school has won.

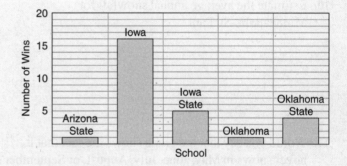

4. Which university has won the most championships since 1970?

5. Has Iowa won more than the other schools combined since 1970? If so, how many more?

6. Would you say that one university has dominated wrestling over the past 27 years?

7. Would a table better represent this data? Explain why or why not.

The line graph at the right represents the average monthly snowfall in inches for Minneapolis-St. Paul, Minnesota.

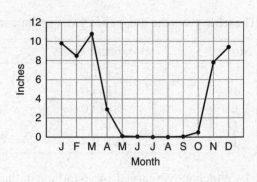

8. Use the graph to determine the month with the most snowfall.

9. Approximately how many inches fall in that month?

10. Estimate the average annual snowfall for Minneapolis-St. Paul.

11. Would you say that the graph shows the fact that it never snows in May, June, July, August, or September? Explain.

In Exercises 1–4, evaluate the expression. Then describe the results in words.

1. $21 \div 3$ **2.** $14 + 5$ **3.** $42 \cdot 3$ **4.** $133 - 17$

In Exercises 5–8, match the verbal description with the variable expression.

5. The product of a number and 5

6. The difference of a number and 5

7. The sum of a number and 5

8. The quotient of a number and 5

A. $y + 5$ **B.** $y \div 5$ **C.** $5a$ **D.** $b - 5$

In Exercises 9–20, evaluate the variable expression when $x = 2$.

9. $x + 2$ **10.** $42 \div x$ **11.** $3x$

12. $4x$ **13.** $x - 2$ **14.** $3 - x$

15. $x - 1$ **16.** $2 - x$ **17.** $5x$

18. $\dfrac{6}{x}$ **19.** $7 + x$ **20.** $7 - x$

In Exercises 21–32, evaluate the expression when $a = 2$ **and** $b = 5$.

21. $b - a$

22. $a \cdot b$

23. $3a + b$

24. $12 - a - b$

25. $a + b$

26. $2 + b + a$

27. $a + b + 5$

28. $3ab$

29. $3b + a$

30. $4 \cdot b \cdot a$

31. $b - a - 1$

32. $a + b - a$

In Exercises 33–35, use the following information:

The estimated daily circulations of the five daily newspapers in a county are shown in the graph to the right.

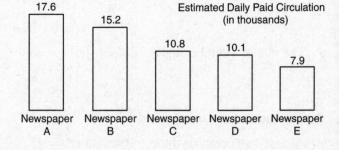

33. About how many more copies of Newspaper A were sold per day than of Newspaper B?

34. About what was the total circulation of the five newspapers?

35. If Newspaper B costs $.50 per paper, about what was the daily income for Newspaper B?

In Exercises 1 and 2, rewrite the power as repeated multiplication. Then evaluate.

1. 3^4

2. 2^5

In Exercises 3–8, write the expression as a power. Then evaluate.

3. $10 \times 10 \times 10 \times 10 \times 10$

4. $7 \times 7 \times 7 \times 7$

5. $15 \times 15 \times 15$

6. $x \cdot x \cdot x \cdot x \cdot x \cdot x$, when $x = 3$

7. $y \cdot y \cdot y \cdot y \cdot y$, when $y = 4$

8. $z \cdot z \cdot z \cdot z$, when $z = 5$

In Exercises 9–14, evaluate the expression when $n = 2$.

9. $n^2 - 4$

10. n^4

11. $(n^2 + 2)^3$

12. $n^5 - 16$

13. $(n - 1)^{17}$

14. n^7

In Exercises 15–20, use rounding to estimate the value of the power. Then use a calculator to check your estimate.

15. 2.9^3 **16.** 11^5 **17.** 0.9^4

18. 99^5 **19.** 0.99^5 **20.** 4.85^2

In Exercises 21–24, complete the statement using <, >, or =.

21. 4^2 (?) 2^4 **22.** 3^5 (?) 5^3

23. 7^3 (?) 3^7 **24.** 3^2 (?) 2^3

25. The closed box shown at right has dimensions 8 in. by 8 in. by 8 in.

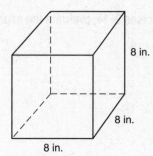

    a. Find the volume of the box.

    b. What is the area of each face of the box?

    c. Is it possible to place another box of volume 420 cubic inches inside of the box shown? Explain.

In Exercises 1–14, evaluate the expression.

1. $3 + 8 \div 2$

2. $18 - 6 \div 2$

3. $4 \cdot 3 \div 4^2$

4. $6^2 - 9 \cdot 4$

5. $(3 + 2) \div 5 \cdot 2^3$

6. $30 - 3^2 + 4 \cdot 5$

7. $3[2^4 \div 4 - 2]$

8. $16 \div 8(2) \times 6$

9. $24 + 4^2 \cdot 6$

10. $64 \div (2)(8) + 12$

11. $[2 + 3(2) + 3^2] - 4^2$

12. $(4 + 6) \div 2 + 5^2$

13. $24 + (3^2 \div 3) \cdot 11$

14. $[(4^2 + 2) \div 2 + 10] - 2$

In Exercises 15–22, use a calculator to evaluate the expression.

15. $36 + 3 \div 12 + 6$

16. $12 - 3^2 + 9 \cdot 6$

17. $100 \cdot 5 \div 5^3$

18. $20 - (2^5 \div 4^2) \cdot 6$

19. $50 - (2 \div 5^2) \cdot 100$

20. $75 + 5^3 - 4^3 \div 2^3$

21. $24 + (2 \cdot 8)^2 \div 4^2 - 6$

22. $18 \cdot 2^3 - 5 \cdot 6 \div 2$

In Exercises 23–30, decide whether the value of the expression is correct. If it is incorrect, insert parentheses to make it correct.

23. $4 + 24 \div 6 = 8$

24. $18 - 6 \div 2 = 6$

25. $6 \cdot 3 - 2 \cdot 3 = 18$

26. $24 - 3 \div 7 + 2 = 5$

27. $5 + 2^2 \div 3 = 3$

28. $8^2 - 4 \div 2 + 2 = 65$

29. $24 \div 4 + 2 - 2^2 = 0$

30. $4^2 - 3^2 \div 3 = 13$

In Exercises 31–34, write a verbal phrase that describes the expression. Then evaluate.

31. $36 \div (9 + 3)$

32. $42 \div 21 + 6$

33. $42 \div (14 \div 2)$

34. $12 - 4 \times 2$

35. You and three friends go to the movies. The group has $40 total. The cost per ticket is $5.25. Each one of the group wants a large soda for $1.25 each, and a box of candy for $1.15 each. Two of the four are willing to share a large buttered popcorn for $3.75 and the other two are going to share a medium unbuttered popcorn for $3.00. Write an expression that represents the total. How much money did the group spend? How much money remains?

In Exercises 1–4, find the perimeter and area of the figure.

1.

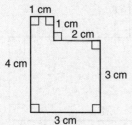

2.

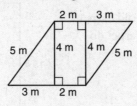

3.

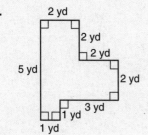

4.

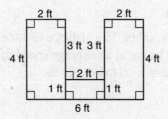

5. Explain in words how you found the area of the figure in Exercise 4.
Copy the figure and divide it into the separate figures you used to find the total area.

In Exercises 6 and 7, use the diagram of the restaurant dining room.

6. The owners of a restaurant want to replace the old carpet in the dining room. How many square feet of carpet do they need to buy?

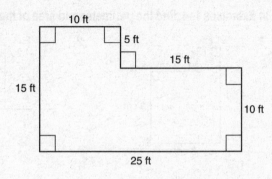

7. How many large tables can fit in the dining room if each requires an area of 25 square feet?

In Exercises 8–10, use the following information.

Your family is taking a trip to visit your grandmother. The distance to your grandmother's house is 300 miles. You travel by car at an average speed of 50 miles per hour. Use the distance formula ($d = r \cdot t$) to answer the following questions.

8. How long will it take to get to your grandmother's house?

9. How far will you travel in 3 hours?

10. How long will it take to get to your grandmother's house if you travel at an average speed of 60 miles per hour?

In Exercises 1 and 2, identify the irrelevant information. Then solve the problem.

1. A theater seats 10,000 people. Tickets for tonight's show cost $14. The theater was built in 1888. How old will the theater be in 2002?

2. Daisy wants to buy a new stereo system. She loves to listen to music. There are two models that she likes. One model costs $360 and the other $540. If her summer job pays $6 per hour, how many hours must she work to afford the less expensive one? How many hours must she work to afford the more expensive one?

In Exercises 3 and 4, identify the irrelevant information. Describe the missing information that is needed to solve the problem.

3. The walls and ceiling of a room have an area of 1000 square feet. The occupant of the room likes blue paint. How many gallons of paint are needed to paint the room?

4. A swimming pool can hold 5000 cubic feet of water. Chlorine is added to the water to keep it free of bacteria. How long will it take to fill the pool with a garden hose?

In Exercises 5–12, describe the pattern. List the next three numbers in the sequence.

5. 5, 10, 15, 20, ?, ?, ?

6. 5, 10, 20, 40, ?, ?, ?

7. 98, 90, 82, 74, ?, ?, ?

8. $\frac{1}{2}, \frac{3}{5}, \frac{5}{8}, \frac{7}{11}$, ?, ?, ?

9. 52, 49, 55, 52, ?, ?, ?

10. 124, 100, 78, 58, ?, ?, ?

11. $\frac{3}{7}, \frac{8}{13}, \frac{13}{19}, \frac{18}{25}$, ?, ?, ?

12. 1024, 512, 256, 128, ?, ?, ?

In Exercises 13–15, use the following information.

Two students form a new club at your school. The club quickly becomes very popular. There are 1024 students that attend your school.

13. If each club member invites one student to join the club each day, and they all accept the invitation, how many days will it take for the club to grow to 32 members?

14. What is the pattern in the growth of the club?

15. How many days will it take for all of the students in the school to join the club?

16. You decide to build a pyramid out of wooden blocks. Each block must rest on the corners of 4 other blocks. If there is one block on top and 36 on the bottom, what is the total number of blocks you will need to complete the pyramid?

In Exercises 1–4, name the property shown.

1. $3 + (7 + 4) = (3 + 7) + 4$ **2.** $5 \cdot (2 \cdot 9) = (5 \cdot 2) \cdot 9$

3. $11(1 + 7) = 11(7 + 1)$ **4.** $6 \cdot 9 \cdot 2 = 9 \cdot 6 \cdot 2$

5. Here is one way to evaluate $(5 \cdot 92) \cdot 20$. Justify each step.

$$(5 \cdot 92) \cdot 20 = (92 \cdot 5) \cdot 20$$
$$= 92 \cdot (5 \cdot 20)$$
$$= 92 \cdot 100$$
$$= 9200$$

In Exercises 6–11, do not evaluate. Use the commutative and associative properties to find the missing number.

6. $49 + 51 = ? + 49$

7. $93 \cdot ? = 74 \cdot 93$

8. $(32 + 61) + 21 = ? + (61 + 21)$

9. $(11 + 23) \cdot 41 = ? \cdot (11 + 23)$

10. $(? + 5) \cdot (17 + 81) = (17 + 81) \cdot (5 + 22)$

11. $(45 \cdot 7) \cdot 56 = ? \cdot (7 \cdot 56)$

In Exercises 12–14, use the commutative and associative properties of addition and mental math to find the sum.

12. $(33 + 33) + (67 + 67)$

13. $(17 + 84) + (83 + 54) + (16 + 46)$

14. $(22 + 57) + 78$

In Exercises 15–17, use the commutative and associative properties of multiplication and mental math to find the product.

15. $(10 \cdot 5) \cdot (7 \cdot 2)$

16. $2 \cdot (73 \cdot 50)$

17. $(10 \cdot 5) \cdot (85 \cdot 20)$

In Exercises 1–4, tell whether the example illustrates the correct use of the distributive property. Justify your answer. If not, rewrite the example so that it does.

1. $4(2 + 5) = 4(2) + 4(5)$

2. $6(a + 4) = 24a$

3. $3(4 - 2z) = 6z$

4. $13(3 + 1) = 39$

In Exercises 5–16, use the distributive property to write an equivalent expression. Then simplify when possible.

5. $2(3 + 5)$

6. $12(4 + 7)$

7. $3(x + 2)$

8. $15(y + 4)$

9. $4(z + 3)$

10. $8(2 + p)$

11. $x(y + 3)$

12. $a(c + 4)$

13. $2(x + y + z)$

14. $z(a + 4 + b)$

15. $f(g + 3 + h)$

16. $10(2 + y + z)$

In Exercises 17–19, use the distributive property to evaluate each expression mentally.

17. $2 \cdot 6 + 2 \cdot 4$

18. $0.5 \cdot 10 + 0.5 \cdot 20$

19. $5 \cdot x - 2 \cdot x$

In Exercises 20–22, use the following information.

You have entered a marathon to raise money for charity. You have received pledges of $.20, $.10, and $.15 per mile that you complete.

20. Write an expression for the total you will earn for the charity if you complete 10 miles.

21. Write an equivalent expression using the distributive property.

22. Evaluate both expressions. Are they equal?

Practice 2.1

Name _____ Date _____

In Exercises 1–4, match the verbal phrase with its variable expression.

A. $2m + 4$ **B.** $\dfrac{n}{2} - 4$ **C.** $10 - p$ **D.** $y - 10$

1. 4 more than twice a number

2. The difference of 10 and a number

3. 4 less than the quotient of a number and 2

4. 10 less than a number

In Exercises 5–15, translate the verbal phrase into a variable expression.

5. 16 plus a number

6. A number divided by 12

7. The quotient of a number and 11

8. 8 times a number

9. 12 less than a number

10. 14 more than 6 times a number

11. 8 minus the product of 5 and a number

12. The sum of 3 times a number and 17

13. The product of 6 and 4 more than a number

14. The quotient of a number and 4 more than another number

15. The difference of 3 times a number and 6 times another number

In Exercises 16–19, translate the verbal phrase into a variable expression.

16. Your allowance plus $5.00

17. 5 years older than your sister

18. Number of players divided by 4

19. 5 times more than the cost to her

In Exercises 20–23, write the variable expression as a word phrase.

20. $5 \times p$

21. $m - 16$

22. $4(x + 2)$

23. $11 + 2y$

24. Suppose you purchased a new mountain bike by making a down payment of $38.70 plus monthly payments of $5.75 each.

    a. Write an algebraic expression that represents your total cost. Let m be the number of monthly payments.

    b. Find the cost if you have to make 30 monthly payments.

In Exercises 1–9, simplify the expression by combining like terms.

1. $3x + x$

2. $4y + 5y$

3. $2z + 6z + 10$

4. $3a + 5b + 6a$

5. $3z + 7 + 6z + 2$

6. $15z + 5 + 6z$

7. $3s + 2t + 8s + 4$

8. $12x + 3y + 4 + 6y$

9. $6x + 2 + 4x + 9$

In Exercises 10–15, tell whether the expression can be simplified.
Explain why or why not.

10. $y + 5y$

11. $3b - 8$

12. $x^2 + 3x$

13. $9y + 2p$

14. $5(z + 7) - 12$

15. $a + 2b - 3c$

16. Describe the steps for simplifying $3y + 6 - y - 2$.

17. Write an expression that has four terms and simplifies to $7z - 15$.

18. Bob sold his car to Jim for $2000. A year later, Jim sold the car to Judy for $1800. The next year, Judy sold the car to Maria for $1600. Based on these sale prices, write an expression for the price Maria may sell the car for t years after she bought it.

In Exercises 19–24, simplify the expression and justify your steps. Then evaluate
the expression when $x = 3$ and $y = 4$.

19. $3x + 2y + 6x$

20. $y + 2(y + 2)$

21. $5(x + y) + 2x$

22. $(3 + x)y + x^2$

23. $xy + x^2 + x^2$

24. $3(x + y) + 2(x + y)$

In Exercises 25 and 26, write an expression for the perimeter. Find the perimeter when x is 1, 2, 3, 4, and 5. Show your results in a table. Describe the pattern in the results as the values of x increase by 1.

25.

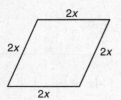

26.

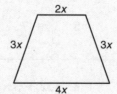

27. You and your family and your best friend and her family are planning a trip to an amusement park. There are two parents and three children in your friend's family, and there is one parent and two children in your family. The price of admission to the park is x dollars for adults and y dollars for youths.

 a. Write an expression for the cost of admission for your family.

 b. Write an expression for the cost of admission for your friend's family.

 c. Write an expression for the total cost for both families combined.

 d. If the price of admission increases from x to $a + 1$ for adults and from y to $b + 2$ for youths, write a new expression for the cost for both families combined. Simplify this expression.

In Exercises 1–4, match the equation with the correct solution.

A. 2   **B.** 5   **C.** 3   **D.** 1

1. $3x - 4 = 11$ **2.** $y^2 + 4 = 13$ **3.** $8 - 3y = 5$ **4.** $16x^2 = 64$

In Exercises 5 and 6, write the equation as a question. Then solve the equation.

5. $3x = 36$ **6.** $z - 5 = 3$

In Exercises 7 and 8, find the number that answers the question.
Show a check to make sure your answer is correct.

7. What number can be added to 5 to obtain 19?   **8.** What number can be divided by 8 to obtain 7?

In Exercises 9–12, decide whether $x = 6$ is a solution of the equation. If it is not, find the correct solution.

9. $2x = 8$ **10.** $19 - x = 13$ **11.** $\dfrac{30}{x} = 5$ **12.** $3(x + 2) = 18$

In Exercises 13 and 14, determine whether the equations have the same solution. Explain your reasoning.

13. a. $3x = 12$

b. $\dfrac{12}{x} = 3$

14. a. $12 - x = 8$

b. $x - 8 = 12$

In Exercises 15–18, solve the equation using mental math.
Check your solution in the original equation.

15. $m + 6 = 11$ **16.** $n - 6 = 7$ **17.** $18 + p = 42$ **18.** $q - 16 = 35$

In Exercises 19 and 20, decide whether the equation is an identity. Explain your answer.

19. $32 - x = 20$

20. $9(x + 3) = 9x + 27$

In Exercises 21–23, use the graph to write an equation. Then use mental math to solve it.

21. The number of farms in 1910 was 3.7 million more than the number in 1870. How many farms were there in 1910?

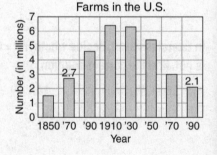

Farms in the U.S.

22. The number in 1950 was two times the number in 1870. How many farms were there in 1950?

23. The number in 1930 divided by the number in 1990 is 3. How many farms were there in 1930?

In Exercises 1–4, match the sentence with the equation.

A. $x - 6 = 12$ **B.** $\dfrac{x}{6} = 12$ **C.** $6x = 12$ **D.** $12 - x = 6$

1. The difference of 12 and x is 6.   **2.** The quotient of x and 6 is 12.

3. 12 equals the difference of x and 6.   **4.** The product of 6 and x is 12.

In Exercises 5–12, write an equation that represents the verbal sentence.

5. The number of cassettes decreased by 5 is 13.

6. $225.75 is the cost of 3 calculators at x dollars each.

7. The number of books divided by 7 equals 9.

8. 32 is the sum of 18 sweatshirts and y.

9. The difference of a and 6 is 13.

10. 45 is the product of 5 and c.

11. The quotient of e and 5 is 40.

12. 15 is 3 more than f.

In Exercises 13–15, use a verbal model, labels, and an algebraic model to answer the question.

13. The quotient of a number and 6 is 21. Find the number.

14. 165 is the product of a number and 11. Find the number.

15. On a recent trip to an audio-video store you purchased four items. The total cost was $39.00. Three items you purchased were for yourself, and the last your sister asked you to buy for her. She now wants to pay you back but you lost the receipt. However, you do know that the three items you purchased for yourself were a cassette single for $2.50, a cassette for $6.50, and a CD for $13.50. How much does your sister owe you for her item?

In Exercises 1–4, copy and complete the solution.

1. $x + 21 = 65$

$x + 21 - \boxed{?} = 65 - \boxed{?}$

$x = \boxed{?}$

2. $58 = y - 32$

$58 + \boxed{?} = y - 32 + \boxed{?}$

$\boxed{?} = y$

3. $z - 28 = 101$

$z - 28 + \boxed{?} = 101 + \boxed{?}$

$z = \boxed{?}$

4. $312 = w + 217$

$312 - \boxed{?} = w + 217 - \boxed{?}$

$\boxed{?} = w$

In Exercises 5–8, use the subtraction property of equality to solve the equation. Then check your solution.

5. $a + 2.2 = 5.7$ **6.** $51 = x + 22$ **7.** $13 + z = 15.3$ **8.** $k + 12 = 17.7$

In Exercises 9–12, use the addition property of equality to solve the equation. Then check your solution.

9. $q - 16 = 23$ **10.** $40 = y - 21$ **11.** $c - 18.2 = 9.3$ **12.** $s - 23 = 12.1$

In Exercises 13–15, solve the equation. Justify your steps and check your solution.

13. $m + 8 = 14$ **14.** $365 = p - 90$ **15.** $32 = t + 4.9$

In Exercises 16–19, write an equation that represents the statement. Then solve the equation.

16. The difference of x and 7 is 28.

17. The sum of y and 2.7 is 8.3.

18. The sum of z and 3.1 is 15.2.

19. The difference of a and 5.01 is 22.7.

In Exercises 20–23, estimate the solution. Then use a calculator to solve the equation.

20. $z - 123.03 = 378.92$

21. $1.609 = k + 0.573$

22. $t + 44.99 = 55.23$

23. $987 = q - 115$

In Exercises 24–26, use the following information.

The top three sales months for T-Shirt sales at a stadium were, in order, December, April, and October(when 1431 shirts were sold).

24. The total of April's sales and October's sales was 2969 shirts. Find April's sales.

25. The difference between December's sales and October's sales was 122 shirts. Find December's sales.

26. The fourth highest month was July. The difference between October's sales and July's sales was 20 shirts. Find July's sales.

In Exercises 1 and 2, copy and complete the solution. Justify each step.

1. $\dfrac{n}{12} = 12$

$\boxed{?} \cdot \dfrac{n}{12} = \boxed{?} \cdot 12$

$n = \boxed{?}$

2. $5p = 7.5$

$\dfrac{5p}{?} = \dfrac{7.5}{?}$

$p = \boxed{?}$

In Exercises 3–10, use the division property of equality to solve the equation. Then check your solution.

3. $5a = 25$ 4. $169 = 13x$ 5. $42 = 6c$ 6. $11z = 154$

7. $22b = 132$ 8. $128 = 16y$ 9. $2.3k = 13.8$ 10. $49m = 343$

In Exercises 11–18, use the multiplication property of equality to solve the equation. Then check your solution.

11. $\dfrac{d}{3} = 9$ 12. $\dfrac{r}{4} = 32$ 13. $33 = \dfrac{t}{11}$ 14. $8.8 = \dfrac{s}{2}$

15. $\dfrac{n}{5} = 25$ 16. $16.1 = \dfrac{p}{4}$ 17. $35 = \dfrac{q}{3.3}$ 18. $\dfrac{w}{12} = 5$

In Exercises 19–22, solve the equation. Justify your steps and check your solution.

19. $10a = 110$ **20.** $7u = 49$ **21.** $\dfrac{d}{13.5} = 0.5$ **22.** $9 = \dfrac{h}{9}$

In Exercises 23–26, estimate the solution. Then use a calculator to solve the equation. Check your answer.

23. $48x = 244.8$ **24.** $\dfrac{q}{3.3} = 10.1$ **25.** $\dfrac{v}{8.9} = 1.01$ **26.** $14k = 72.8$

27. Marta is buying new carpet for three rooms of her house. The floor of the living room has an area of 200 ft². The floor of the master bedroom covers three fourths as much area as the living room. The floor of the second bedroom covers one half as much area as the master bedroom. Write and solve an equation to determine the minimum square feet of carpet Marta needs to purchase to cover the floors of the three rooms.

28. Eric ran one mile on Monday. If he doubles his running distance each day, how many miles will he run on Friday? Explain what method you used to solve the problem.

In Exercises 29 and 30, write an equation that relates the length and the width of the rectangle to its area. Then solve the equation to find the missing side length.

29.

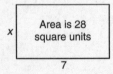

x | Area is 28 square units

7

30.

x | Area is 54 square units

9

1. You plan to drive 400 miles to visit relatives. Your goal is to make it there in 12 hours or less. There are a few stops on the way that you would like to make. You travel at 50 miles per hour and you want to spend at least 60 minutes at each stop. Arrange the steps below to find the number of stops you can make while not exceeding your goal.

A. $60s + 480 = 720$

B. You can make four stops.

C. Minutes for stops + Minutes to drive = Goal of 12 hours (720 minutes)

D. $s = 4$

E. $60(4) + 480 = 240 + 480 = 720$

F. Number of stops = s

   Minutes for stops = $60s$

   Minutes to drive = $\dfrac{400 \text{ miles}}{50 \text{ miles per hour}} = 8$ hours (480 minutes)

   Goal of 12 hours = 720 (minutes)

2. A forest covers 100 square miles of land. An aerial survey has determined that there are approximately 100,000 trees per square mile. Explain how to find the total number of trees in the forest.

In Exercises 3–5, use the following information.

You are fencing a rectangular corral to keep horses. The region's length is 48 more feet than its width. The perimeter of the region is 184 feet.

3. Write a verbal model that relates the length, the width, and the perimeter to find the dimensions of the region. Assign labels to the three parts of the verbal model.

4. Write and solve an algebraic model using the verbal model and labels from Exercise 3.

5. Check your solution from Exercise 4 for reasonableness.

In Exercises 6–8, use the following information.

You are a salesperson at the local sporting goods store. Your monthly earnings

are a combination of your monthly base salary plus your sales commission.

Your monthly salary is $300 and your sales commission is $\frac{1}{25}$ of your monthly sales.

6. Write a verbal model that relates your sales commission rate, your
   sales commission, and your monthly sales to find how much you
   make during a month when your sales totaled $2600. Assign labels to
   each part of the verbal model.

7. Write and solve an algebraic model using the verbal model and labels from Exercise 6.

8. Check your solution from Exercise 7 for reasonableness.

Decide whether the answer seems reasonable. Explain.

9. Sarah is baby-sitting for $5 per hour. She is trying to save enough
   money to buy a dress she saw in a magazine. The dress costs $500.
   She estimates that she will have to work 40 hours to buy the dress.

In Exercises 1–4, decide whether the number is a solution of the inequality $x + 7 > 13$. Explain why or why not.

1. 10   **2.** 5   **3.** 6   **4.** 3

In Exercises 5–8, write the inequality that represents the sentence. Then solve the inequality.

5. d minus 5 is less than or equal to 4.25.

6. The sum of y and 7 is greater than 10.

7. x times 40 is less than 120.

8. 69 is greater than the product of a and 3.

In Exercises 9–14, list two solutions of the inequality.

9. $x \geq 3$ **10.** $y < 1.5$ **11.** $36 < x$

12. $300 \geq z$ **13.** $a < 11.5$ **14.** $b \geq 0.01$

In Exercises 15–26, solve the inequality. Justify each step of the solution.

15. $x + 3 < 8$

16. $y - 2 \geq 10$

17. $3z < 15$

18. $\dfrac{a}{2} > 11$

19. $b - 4 < 6$

20. $15 > c - 12$

21. $4p < 60$

22. $\dfrac{q}{4} > 12.2$

23. $x - 2.5 < 7.2$

24. $42 > \dfrac{c}{7}$

25. $105.5 \geq y - 5$

26. $11.2 < 4z$

27. Write a true numerical inequality, such as $9 > 5$. Subtract 3 from each side of your inequality. Is the inequality still true? What general rule does your answer suggest?

28. Your summer job pays $5 per hour. You are trying to save enough money to buy a new bicycle that costs $250. Write and solve an inequality to determine the minimum number of hours you must work to earn enough to buy the bicycle.

In Exercises 1 and 2, draw a number line and plot the integers.

1. $-3, 1, -2$

2. $0, 5, -1$

In Exercises 3–6, order the integers from least to greatest.

3. $-6, 5, -4, 3, 2$

4. $-10, 8, -7, 6, 0$

5. $-2, 2, -3, 4, 1$

6. $-1, 1, 0, 2, -3$

In Exercises 7–10, write the integer that represents the situation.

7. 700 feet above sea level

8. A loss of 57 dollars

9. A 15 yard gain

10. A gain of 20 pounds

In Exercises 11–14, evaluate the absolute value.

11. $|-13|$

12. $|7|$

13. $|-4|$

14. $|99|$

In Exercises 15–20, write the opposite of the integer.

15. 3

16. -2

17. 5

18. -6

19. -10

20. -100

In Exercises 21 and 22, find a value or values of x that make the statement true.

21. $|x| = 9$

22. $-x = 2$

In Exercises 23–26, use the number line to estimate the number of days between the events.

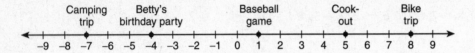

Camping trip	Betty's birthday party		Baseball game		Cook-out		Bike trip

23. Bike trip and cook out

24. Birthday party and cook out

25. Baseball game and bike trip

26. Birthday party and camping trip

In Exercises 27–29, use the following:

On a certain day in January the temperature in Anchorage, Alaska was 15° below zero. In St. Paul, Minnesota it was 5° above zero. In San Diego, California it was 50° above zero. And in Tampa, Florida, it was 75° above zero.

27. Draw a number line showing these temperatures.

28. How much warmer is it in Tampa than in St. Paul?

29. How much colder is it in Anchorage than in San Diego?

In Exercises 1–12, use a number line to find the sum.

1. $7 + (-6)$

2. $-8 + 3$

3. $-4 + (-2)$

4. $-4 + 4$

5. $-3 + 6$

6. $9 + (-5)$

7. $4 + (-8) + 2$

8. $14 + (-10)$

9. $3 + (-4) + 1$

10. $11 + 1 + (-8)$

11. $12 + (-6)$

12. $-2 + (-6) + 5$

In Exercises 13–16, use the given information to write a sum of integers. Then use a number line to find the sum and solve the problem.

13. The temperature at 6 A.M. was 1° Celsius. It had risen 10° by 11 A.M. What was the temperature at 11 A.M.?

14. You need $4 to buy lunch. You have $2. How much more money do you need to buy lunch?

15. A baseball team's average score for each game is 5 runs. On their last game of the season, the team scored 3 runs above the average. How many runs did the team score?

16. The average height of the students in a seventh grade class is 59 inches. One student is 8 inches taller than the average. How tall is this student?

In Exercises 17–20, use the information and this table.

The table shows the lap times (in seconds) of four cars attempting to qualify for a race. Any car that completes the four laps in less than five minutes will qualify.

Car	Lap 1	Lap 2	Lap 3	Lap 4
Red	72	70	69	74
Green	75	76	71	73
Blue	77	75	72	76
Yellow	68	80	72	70

17. Find the total time it took for each car to complete the four laps.

18. Which car did not qualify for the race?

19. What is the time difference between the fastest and slowest cars?

20. What is the time difference between the third and second fastest cars?

In Exercises 21 and 22, find a pair of integers whose sum is – 2. (Use the integers labeled *a*, *b*, *c*, and *d*.)

21.

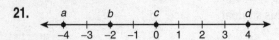

22.

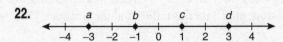

In Exercises 1–12, find the sum.

1. $3 + 12$

2. $-6 + (-3)$

3. $-12 + (-12)$

4. $6 + 16$

5. $-5 + 5$

6. $12 + (-18)$

7. $-19 + 12$

8. $26 + (-26)$

9. $4 + 0$

10. $0 + (-11)$

11. $15 + (-2)$

12. $-12 + 0$

In Exercises 13–21, find the sum.

13. $6 + (-2) + (-8)$

14. $-6 + (-2) + 10$

15. $6 + (-7) + (-8)$

16. $-16 + 15 + (-3)$

17. $-10 + 11 + (-2)$

18. $-10 + 6 + (-8)$

19. $-10 + (-6) + (-15)$

20. $6 + (-5) + (-4)$

21. $10 + (-2) + 13$

In Exercises 22–25, simplify the expression.

22. $-6x + 10x + (-2x)$

23. $17x + (-6x) + 4$

24. $20x + (-16x) + (-2x)$

25. $-3x + 12x + 10$

In Exercises 26–31, simplify the expression. Then evaluate the expression when $x = 3$.

26. $6x + (-2x) + x + 7$

27. $6 + (-3x) + 11x$

28. $4x + (-x) + (-2x)$

29. $9x + 6 + (-3x) + 2$

30. $15x + (-3x) + 7x + 4$

31. $11x + (-6x) + 11$

32. On Monday you purchased $100 worth of stock. The value of the stock on Monday was $6 per share. Tuesday it rose $2. Wednesday it fell $4. Thursday it rose $3. Friday it fell $2. What is the week ending price per share?

33. You are in an elevator in a 50 story building. You are on the 25th floor. You remain on the elevator as passengers get on and off. What floor are you on an hour later, if the elevator moves as follows: up 12, down 23, up 35, down 12, down 3, and up 16?

In Exercises 1–9, find the difference.

1. $3 - 7$

2. $-4 - (-3)$

3. $6 - (-8)$

4. $10 - (-2)$

5. $-23 - 2$

6. $12 - (-8)$

7. $14 - (-3)$

8. $16 - (-16)$

9. $-16 - 16$

In Exercises 10–13, evaluate the expression.

10. $-4 + 9 - 3$

11. $8 + 16 - 5$

12. $4 + 2 - (-13)$

13. $6 - (-8) + 14$

In Exercises 14–19, evaluate the expression when $a = 2$ and when $a = -2$.

14. $a - 3$

15. $3 - a$

16. $a - 2$

17. $6 - a$

18. $a - a$

19. $a + a$

In Exercises 20 and 21, rewrite the expression as a sum. Identify the terms.
If possible, simplify the expression.

20. $4x - 2x + 8$

21. $10x - 12 - 5$

In Exercises 22–27, simplify the expression. Then evaluate the expression when *x* = 3.

22. $8x - 2x - 7$ **23.** $11x - 2x + 2$ **24.** $12x - (-3x) - 3$

25. $30x - 25x - 3x$ **26.** $-4x - (-16x)$ **27.** $6 - (-2x) - 3x$

In Exercises 28 and 29, find values for *a* and *b* so that the statement is true.
(There are many correct answers.)

28. *a* is positive, *b* is positive, and $b - a$ is negative.

29. *a* is negative, *b* is negative, and $b - a$ is positive.

In Exercises 30–32, use the table which shows the highest and lowest elevations on the continents. Positive numbers are elevations in feet above sea level and negative numbers are elevations in feet below sea level.

Continent	Highest Point	Feet above sea level	Lowest point	Feet below sea level
Asia	Mt. Everest	29,028	Dead Sea	−1312
North America	Mt. McKinley	20,320	Death Valley	−282
Africa	Mt. Kilimanjaro	19,340	Lake Assal	−512
Europe	Mt. Elbrus	18,510	Caspian Sea	−92

30. Find the difference between the highest point and lowest point on each continent.

31. Find the difference between the lowest points in Asia and North America.

32. Find the difference between the highest points in Africa and Europe.

In Exercises 1–9, find the product.

1. $6 \cdot 5$

2. $8(10)$

3. $-3 \cdot (-2)$

4. $-15 \cdot 3$

5. $10 \cdot (-3)$

6. $7 \cdot (-4)$

7. $(-3)(-7)$

8. $(0)(-30)$

9. $(4)(0)$

In Exercises 10–15, match the property with an example that illustrates how the property applies to integers.

10. Commutative property of multiplication

    A. $5(-2 + 3) = 5(-2) + 5(3)$

11. Associative property of multiplication

    B. $3 \cdot 9 = 9 \cdot 3$

12. Commutative property of addition

    C. $2 \cdot (7 \cdot 8) = (2 \cdot 7) \cdot 8$

13. Distributive property

    D. $-8 \cdot 1 = -8$

14. Identity property of multiplication

    E. $11 + (-8) = -8 + 11$

15. Property of -1

    F. $-2(-4) = 8$

In Exercises 16–18, simplify the expression. Tell what properties you use.

16. $4x + 6 - 2x$

17. $11x + x + 7 - 2x$

18. $-5x + 8 + 5x$

In Exercises 19–22, simplify the expression. Then evaluate the expression when $n = -3$.

19. $-4n + 9 - 2n$

20. $6n + 9 - 3n + 11$

21. $8 + n - 7n$

22. $5n + 9 - 4n + n$

In Exercises 23 and 24, answer the question and give an example to support your answer.

23. Is the product of five negative numbers positive or negative?

24. Is the product of six negative numbers positive or negative?

In Exercises 25–27, decide whether the expression is positive or negative when the value of *x* is not zero. Explain your reasoning.

25. x^4　　　　　　**26.** $-3x^4$　　　　　　**27.** $5x^4$

In Exercises 28–30, use the distributive property to write an equivalent expression.

28. $-7(x + 2)$　　　　　**29.** $-3(-4 + x)$　　　　　**30.** $-6(-5 + x)$

In Exercises 31–33, evaluate the expression when *x* = 3 and *y* = –4.

31. xy　　　　　　**32.** x^2y　　　　　　**33.** $-y$

In Exercises 34–36, use the rectangle at the right. The rectangle has an area of 24 square units. The base of the rectangle rests on a number line.

34. If $b = -2$, what is a?

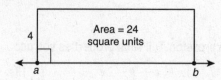

35. If $b = 2$, what is a?

36. If $b = -10$, what is a?

In Exercises 1–11, find the quotient. If the quotient is undefined, say so.

1. $\dfrac{96}{3}$

2. $\dfrac{180}{4}$

3. $\dfrac{-512}{16}$

4. $-208 \div (-8)$

5. $288 \div (-16)$

6. $\dfrac{0}{-36}$

7. $\dfrac{100}{0}$

8. $0 \div 327$

9. $-1008 \div (-21)$

10. $2730 \div (-65)$

11. $57 \div 0$

In Exercises 12–15, evaluate the expression when $x = 4$ and when $x = -8$.

12. $\dfrac{16}{x}$

13. $\dfrac{-32}{x}$

14. $\dfrac{x}{-2}$

15. $\dfrac{-x}{4}$

In Exercises 16–19, evaluate the expression. Follow the order of operations.

16. $(4-9) \div 5$

17. $22 - 12 \div 2$

18. $\dfrac{3-5+9}{-7}$

19. $(-7)^2 - 4 + 6^2$

In Exercises 20–22, evaluate the expression when $x = -3$, $y = 2$, and $z = -4$.

20. xz

21. $\dfrac{-6y}{x}$

22. $\dfrac{xz}{y}$

In Exercises 23 and 24, find the average of the numbers.

23. $18, 11, 15, 17, 13, 16$

24. $-8, -6, -5, -8, -7, -2$

In Exercises 25 and 26, use the table that shows the times that a 100-meter freestyle swimmer had in her trials. The table also shows how the swimmer deviated from a team average of 55 seconds.

25. Find the average of the deviations. Use the result to find the swimmer's average time in seconds.

Trial	Time (in seconds)	Deviation (in hundredths of a second)
1	58.59	359
2	56.65	165
3	55.67	67
4	54.50	−50
5	54.79	−21

26. The swimmer has two more trials. Predict whether her times for the next two trials will be more or less than the average time you found in Exercise 25. Explain your prediction.

In Exercises 1–6, match the equation with one of the solutions below.

A. -32 **B.** 90 **C.** 0 **D.** -7 **E.** -3 **F.** -6

1. $t - 5 + 2 = -3$ **2.** $x - 3x = 64$ **3.** $\dfrac{p}{3} = 41 - 11$

4. $y + 4y = -30 - 5$ **5.** $\dfrac{-24}{q} = 16 - 12$ **6.** $2x + 3x = -15$

In Exercises 7–10, decide whether the value of the variable is a solution of the equation. If it is not, find the solution.

7. $x + 5 = 8, x = 3$ **8.** $y - 6 = -10, y = 4$

9. $-32 = -16b, b = 2$ **10.** $\dfrac{m}{-2} = 24, m = -12$

In Exercises 11–22, solve the equation. Check your solution.

11. $c - 5 = -2$ **12.** $y + 6 = 3$ **13.** $z - 5 = 12$ **14.** $-21 = a - 12$

15. $b + 4 = -6$ **16.** $c - 2 = -10$ **17.** $-72 = 24d$ **18.** $-3e = -48$

19. $\dfrac{f}{-3} = -11$ **20.** $-22 = -11g$ **21.** $3h = -9$ **22.** $\dfrac{j}{2} = -8$

3.7

Name _____ Date _____

In Exercises 23–28, tell whether the solution of the equation is positive or negative. Explain your answer. Then check your answer by using a calculator to solve the equation.

23. $-2351 = t + 205$

24. $m - 216 = 3864$

25. $-4428 = -123n$

26. $\dfrac{p}{-23} = 58$

27. $\dfrac{q}{22} = -24$

28. $-32r = -8096$

In Exercises 29 and 30, write an algebraic equation for the sentence. Then solve the equation and write your conclusion as a sentence.

29. The sum of x and 3 is -6.

30. The product of z and -3 is -27.

In Exercises 31 and 32 use the following information.

The bill (including parts and labor) for the repair of an automobile was $349. The cost for parts was $285. Therefore, the total cost of labor was $64. The labor rate was $32 per hour.

31. Use the verbal model

$$\boxed{\begin{array}{c}\text{Total cost} \\ \text{of labor}\end{array}} = \boxed{\begin{array}{c}\text{Cost of} \\ \text{labor per hour}\end{array}} \cdot \boxed{\begin{array}{c}\text{The number} \\ \text{of hours}\end{array}}$$

to write an algebraic model for the cost of labor. Let t represent the number of hours of labor.

32. Determine the number of hours of labor required.

Practice **3.8**   Name _____ Date _____

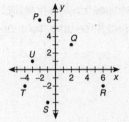

In Exercises 1–6, match the ordered pair with its point in the coordinate plane. Name the quadrant that contains the point.

1. $(-1, -4)$ **2.** $(2, 3)$

3. $(6, -2)$ **4.** $(-2, 6)$

5. $(-3, 1)$ **6.** $(-4, -2)$

In Exercises 7–10, plot all the points in the same coordinate plane. Name the quadrant that contains each point.

7. $(6, -2)$ **8.** $(3, 4)$ **9.** $(-2, -5)$ **10.** $(-3, 2)$

In Exercises 11 and 12, plot the points in a coordinate plane. Connect the points to form a rectangle. Find the perimeter and the area of the rectangle.

11. $A(2, 1), B(5, 1), C(2, 2),$ and $D(5,2)$ **12.** $A(-1, 5), B(-1, -4), C(3, 5),$ and $D(3, -4)$

Name _____ Date _____

In Exercises 13–15, show that the ordered pair is a solution of the equation. Then find three other solutions.

13. $2 + x = y$; $(-12, -10)$ **14.** $y - 3 = x$; $(6, 9)$ **15.** $x - y = 10$; $(12, 2)$

In Exercises 16 and 17, make a table of values that shows four solutions of the equation. Then plot the solutions. Draw a line through the points to represent all the solutions of the equation.

16. $y = 1 - x$ **17.** $x + y = 4$

In Exercises 18–21, use the following.

The graph shows the value of an automobile, which was purchased new for \$25,000, based on the number of years you own it.

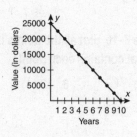

18. After 3 years, what is the value of the car?

19. After 6 years, what is the value of the car?

20. The value is given by the verbal model.

| Value | = | Original value | − | \$2500 | · | Number of years owned |

Create an algebraic model from the verbal model. Let t represent the number of years you own the car, and V represent the value of the car.

21. Find three solutions of your equation.

In Exercises 1–3, tell whether the data in the scatter plot show a *positive correlation*, a *negative correlation*, or *no obvious correlation*.

1.
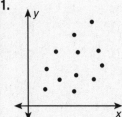

2.
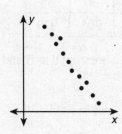

3.
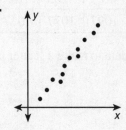

In Exercises 4–6, decide whether the two quantities have a *positive correlation*, a *negative correlation*, or *no correlation*. **Explain your reasoning.**

4. The number of study hours and test scores

5. The number of pets you own and your age

6. The number of hours you watch TV and your test scores

In Exercises 7–10, use the data in the table. The table compares *h,* the altitude in thousands of feet, and *v,* the speed of sound in feet per second.

h	0	5	10	15	20	25	30	35
v	1116	1097	1077	1057	1036	1015	995	973

7. Use the data to make a scatter plot. Put *h* on the horizontal axis and *v* on the vertical axis.

8. Use your scatter plot to describe the correlation of the data. Draw a line that shows the trend.

9. Use your line to estimate the speed of sound at 12,500 feet.

10. Use your line to estimate the altitude at which the speed of sound is 1000 feet/second.

In Exercises 11–13, use the scatter plot at the right. The scatter plot shows the average salaries including fringe benefits for Professors of Public Institutions of Higher Education in thousands of dollars for years 1988 through 1994 where *t* represents the number of years after 1988.

11. What was the average salary in 1991?

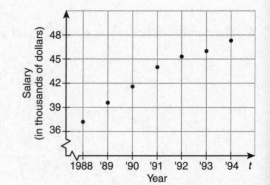

12. How is the salary and the year related? Explain.

13. Estimate the average salary in the year 1998.

In Exercises 1 and 2, complete the solution. Explain your reasoning.

1.
$$5x - 10 = 15$$
$$5x - 10 + \boxed{?} = 15 + \boxed{?}$$
$$5x = \boxed{?}$$
$$\frac{5x}{?} = \boxed{?}$$
$$x = \boxed{?}$$

2.
$$9x + 18 = 72$$
$$9x + 18 - \boxed{?} = 72 - \boxed{?}$$
$$9x = \boxed{?}$$
$$\frac{9x}{\boxed{?}} = \boxed{?}$$
$$x = \boxed{?}$$

In Exercises 3–11, solve the equation. Then check your solution.

3. $2x - 8 = 10$

4. $3x - 7 = 2$

5. $4x + 1 = -3$

6. $\dfrac{t}{2} - 7 = -3$

7. $\dfrac{z}{3} + 4 = -1$

8. $\dfrac{w}{5} - 2 = -7$

9. $6m - 210 = 6$

10. $2x + 1 = 13$

11. $\dfrac{z}{-3} - 4 = -4$

In Exercises 12 and 13, the upper and lower line segments have the same length. Write an equation relating the lengths and solve for x.

12.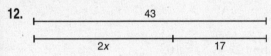

13.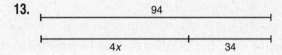

In Exercises 14–17, write the sentence as an equation. Then solve the equation and check your solution.

14. 2 times a number, plus 3 is 13.

15. 6 times a number, plus 11 is 65.

16. The quotient of a number and 3, plus 2 is -7.

17. A number divided by four, minus 6 is 1.

18. The length of a rectangular tennis court is six feet more than twice the width. What is the width of the court if the length is 78 feet?

    a. Write and solve an equation to find the width.

    b. Answer the question. Then check your solution.

19. Describe a real-life situation that can be modeled by the equation $2x + 5 = 10$.

In Exercises 1–4, decide whether the given value is a solution of the equation. If not, find the solution.

1. $6x - 2x - 3 = 5; x = 1$

2. $3y + 2 + 5y = -14; y = 2$

3. $5a - 16 + 2a - 2 = -4; a = 2$

4. $-6 = 4 + 4t - 2t + 16; t = -13$

In Exercises 5–13, solve the equation. Check your solution.

5. $6x - 2x + 11 = -5$

6. $3y - 6 - 2y = 6$

7. $36 = 10a - 12 - 7a$

8. $11m - 6 - 5m = 60$

9. $14n - 12n + 6 = 32$

10. $17p - p - 6 = -38$

11. $5x - 3x + 11x = -91$

12. $11q - 3q + 5q = -39$

13. $10x - 4x - 11 = 1$

In Exercises 14 and 15, write an equation that represents the sentence. Then solve the equation.

14. The sum of $2x$ and $5x$ and $-3x$ and -3 is 9.

15. 11 subtracted from the sum of $7y$ and $2y$ is -38.

In Exercises 16 and 17, use the given information to write an equation. Then solve the equation, and find the angles.

16. The sum of the measures of these two angles is 180°.

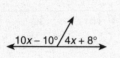

17. The sum of the measures of the angles of this quadrilateral is 360°.

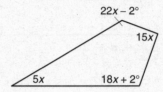

18. You have a summer job as a lifeguard at a pool. The table shows the number of hours you worked each day during a week. During that week, you earned $323.30. You earn x dollars per hour.

S	M	T	W	T	F	S
8	7	7	4	7	10	10

a. Write an equation that represents the amount you earned that week.

b. Solve the equation to find the amount you get paid per hour.

In Exercises 1 and 2, copy and complete the solution.

1. $-7x + 55 = 20$

$-7x + 55 - \boxed{?} = 20 - \boxed{?}$

$-7x = \boxed{?}$

$\dfrac{7x}{?} = \dfrac{10}{10}$

$x = \boxed{?}$

2. $-101 = -5y - 1$

$-101 + \boxed{?} = -5y - 1 + \boxed{?}$

$\boxed{?} = -5y$

$\dfrac{\boxed{?}}{\boxed{?}} = \dfrac{-5y}{\boxed{?}}$

$\boxed{?} = y$

In Exercises 3–14, solve the equation.

3. $3y - 12 = 18$

4. $2x + 11 = -19$

5. $-z + 7 = -3$

6. $2m - 12 = 6$

7. $-4t + 6 = -10$

8. $18y - 6 = -24$

9. $-13t + 10 = -16$

10. $2x - 1 = 19$

11. $2x + x - 6 = 3$

12. $4x - 3x = 10$

13. $2x + 10 = -8$

14. $3x - 6 = 18$

15. The sum of four times a number and 16 is 100. Find the number. Write an equation and solve it.

16. The difference of three times a number and 23 is 34. Find the number.
Write an equation and solve it.

17. The sum of a number and 27 is 40. Find the number. Write an equation
and solve it.

18. −13 is the difference of a number multiplied by 5 and 8. Find the number.
Write an equation and solve it.

19. A traffic sign has the shape of an equilateral triangle. The perimeter
of the sign is 225 centimeters. Find the length of the sides of the sign.
(An equilateral triangle is one whose sides have the same length.)

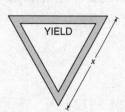

20. A rectangle has a perimeter of 78 inches. Its length is 6 inches more
than twice its width.

    a. Make a sketch of the rectangle and label its sides.

    b. Find the rectangle's length and width.

21. In 1996, the salary of the governor of New York was about $10,000 more
than two times the salary of the governor of Arkansas. The total of the two
salaries was $190,000. Find the 1996 salaries of each state's governor.

In Exercises 1 and 2, describe and correct the error.

1. $3x - 6x + 2 = 8$
$3x + 2 = 8$
$3x = 6$
$x = 2$

2. $4(x - 2) + 6 = 18$
$4x - 2 + 6 = 18$
$4x + 4 = 18$
$4x = 14$
$x = 3$

In Exercises 3–11, solve the equation. Check your solution.

3. $3x + 2(x - 1) = 8$

4. $6 = 3y + 3(y - 6)$

5. $6(2 - r) = -18$

6. $8(p + 1) + 3p = -14$

7. $3(t - 4) + 6 = 0$

8. $6(x - 4) + 3x = 3$

9. $5x - 4x + 2 = -3$

10. $16 = -2(q + 2)$

11. $-5(y + 3) = 25$

12. Solve the equation $2(x + 7) = -26$ in two ways.

    a. Use the distributive property first.

    b. Divide by the same number first.

    c. Which way do you prefer? Why?

13. Solve the equation $-3(x - 11) = 12$ in two ways.

    a. Use the distributive property first.

    b. Divide by the same number first.

    c. Which way do you prefer? Why?

14. Write an equation for the area of the rectangle. Then solve for x.

$$x + 5$$

6 | Area is 42 square units

15. A grocer wants to mix x pounds of cashew nuts worth \$7.00 per pound with 9 pounds of peanuts worth \$3.00 per pound to obtain $(9 + x)$ pounds of mixture worth \$5.00 per pound. Use the verbal model and labels to write an equation and find the number of pounds of cashews required to obtain the specified mixture.

Verbal Model	Total cost of mixed nuts	$-$	Total cost of cashews	$=$	Total cost of peanuts

Labels   Cost per pound of cashews = \$7.00
Number of pounds of cashews = x
Cost per pound of peanuts = \$3.00
Number of pounds of peanuts = 9
Cost per pound of mixed nuts = \$5.00
Number of pounds of mixed nuts = $(9 + x)$ pounds

In Exercises 1–12, solve the equation. Check your solution.

1. $2z = 5 + 3z$

2. $3(3m - 4) = 7m$

3. $6(s - 1) = 2(3 + 4s)$

4. $5x + 12 = 3x$

5. $-5x + 11 = 6x$

6. $8x + 12 = 4x - 4$

7. $-3x + 2 = -7x - 22$

8. $5(x + 3) = 4(x - 4)$

9. $2(x - 7) = 5(x + 2)$

10. $-16 - 8t = 7(t + 2)$

11. $8(3 - y) = 3y + 2$

12. $10(3x + 1) = 2(10x - 5)$

In Exercises 13 and 14, write and solve the equation implied by the model.

13.

x x x 14

x 20

14.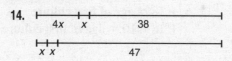

$4x$ x 38

x x 47

In Exercises 15 and 16, write and solve the equation described.

15. Two less than four times a number is equal to two more than three times the same number.

16. Four times the sum of a number and three is equal to eight more than twice the same number.

17. Find the value of x so that the rectangle and the triangle have the same perimeter. What is the perimeter?

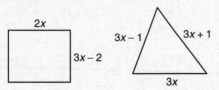

18. Find the value of x so that the figure is a square. What is the length of the sides?

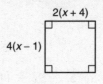

19. One bacterial culture is 18 days older than a second bacterial culture. In 10 days the first culture will be twice the age of the second. Use the verbal model and the labels to write and solve an algebraic equation. Find the present age of the two cultures.

Verbal model

$$\boxed{\begin{array}{c}\text{Age of first culture} \\ \text{in 10 days}\end{array}} = 2 \cdot \boxed{\begin{array}{c}\text{Age of second culture} \\ \text{in 10 days}\end{array}}$$

Labels

x = age of second culture

$x + 10$ = age of second culture in 10 days

$x + 18$ = age of first culture

$x + 18 + 10$ = age of first culture in 10 days

In Exercises 1–7, use the following information.

One long distance phone company charges $2 for the first minute and
$.15 for each additional minute. Another company charges $2.50 for the
first minute and $.10 for each additional minute. For what length of a
phone call would the two companies have the same charge?

1. Show how to use a table and graph to solve the problem.

2. Write a verbal model.

3. Assign labels to each part of the model. (Hint: let t represent the length of
   the phone call, and use $t - 1$ to count the number of minutes after the first.)

4. Write an algebraic model.

5. Solve the algebraic model.

6. For how long of a phone call will each company have the same charge?

7. How much is that phone call?

8. You own a small business that produces bicycle helmets. You want to determine how many helmets must be sold to break even. Your costs are $2500 plus $12 in materials for each helmet. You sell each helmet for $52. Write an algebraic model. Then solve. How many helmets must you sell to break even?

In Exercises 1 and 2, copy and complete the steps. You may use a calculator if you wish. Round each answer to the nearest tenth.

1. $2.3(5.2x - 8.1) = 22.5$

$\boxed{?}x - 18.63 = 22.5$

$\boxed{?}x = \boxed{?}$

$x = \boxed{?}$

2. $0.7(7.3x - 9.8) = 21.4$

$5.11x - \boxed{?} = 21.4$

$5.11x = \boxed{?}$

$x = \boxed{?}$

In Exercises 3–10, solve the equation. Round your answer to the nearest tenth.

3. $4x + 5 = -9$

4. $12y + 1 = 14$

5. $26x - 4 = 25$

6. $13 - 12t = -7$

7. $3(2x - 4) = -6x + 7$

8. $22x - 4 = 5(7 - 2x)$

9. $1.2x + 21.3 = -4.6$

10. $3.21(4.2x - 5.1) = 18.92$

In Exercises 11–16, you may use a calculator if you wish. Round your answer to the nearest hundredth.

11. $0.25t - 11.6 = 2.45t$

12. $2.4x + 11.8 = 7.2x - 26.4$

13. $4.2(4.5x - 31.2) = -4.2x$

14. $13.6x - 4.2 = 6.1(2.5x - 4)$

15. $3.25x - 6.7 = -4.2(3.6x - 4.5)$

16. $19.2(3.5 - 4.1x) = 7.2(8.7x - 4.9)$

17. You eat at a fine Italian restaurant. The gratuity (tip) rate is 0.15 of the price of a meal and the total bill is $29.50. Let p represent the price of the meal. Solve $p + 0.15p = 29.50$ to find the price of the meal.

18. You purchase an item. The sales tax rate is 0.055 of the price of an item and the total cost is $5.96. Let p represent the price of the item (not including sales tax). Solve $p + 0.055p = 5.96$ to find the price of the item.

19. You wish to eat at a neighborhood diner where the special is 12¢ wings. You have $5. You know you are going to have two sodas for 75¢ each. If you are really hungry, how many wings can you order?

20. You are a salesperson who receives $15 per day for meals and 22¢ per mile driven on the job. Your average reimbursement per day is $27.49. Using this amount, estimate the average number of miles you drive per day.

In Exercises 1–4, find the mean, median, and mode of the data.

1. 30, 32, 31, 30, 29, 34

2. 16.5, 18.7, 19.2, 17.3, 18.4, 16.2, 17.6, 16.9

3. 7, 8, 10, 12, 6, 8, 9, 8, 9, 11, 9, 8, 12

4. 42, 48, 43, 48, 51, 51, 48, 46, 46

In Exercises 5–7, use the line plot at the right.

5. How many numbers are represented in the line plot?

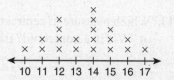

6. Find the mean, median, and mode of the numbers.

7. Describe a real-life situation that can be represented by the line plot.

In Exercises 8–10, which measure of central tendency best represents the data? Explain your reasoning.

8. The favorite colors of 24 students from a second grade class.

9. The prices on a used car lot with a small number of very expensive cars.

10. The number of hours of study time each week by a college freshman.

In Exercises 11–13, use the picture graph, which shows the number of TV sets in each household on a particular street.

11. How many households have 3 TV's?

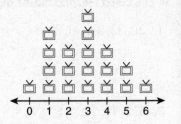

12. Find the mean, median, and mode number of TV's.

13. Which measure of central tendency best represents the number of TV's in a household? Explain.

In Exercises 14 and 15, use the table below. The data in the table gives the prices of eight homes sold in a new housing development.

Home	1	2	3	4	5	6	7	8
Price	56,000	68,000	96,000	62,000	58,000	63,000	69,000	96,000

14. Find the mean, median, and mode of the data.

15. Which measure of central tendency best represents the data? Explain.

In Exercises 1–3, determine if the number is *prime* or *composite*?
Explain your answer.

1. 39

2. 41

3. 57

In Exercises 4–6, write the prime factorization represented by the factor tree.
Use exponents for repeated factors if necessary.

4.

5.

6.

In Exercises 7–12, write the prime factorization of the number. Use exponents for
repeated factors if necessary.

7. 42

8. 64

9. 84

10. 144

11. 200

12. 180

In Exercises 13–16, factor the number or expression.

13. -36 **14.** -45 **15.** $24x^2$ **16.** $16a^3b^2$

In Exercises 17–19, use mental math to find a number that fits the given description.

17. A number with factors of 4 and 13.

18. An expression with factors of z and an odd number.

19. An expression with factors of 2, -3, and n^2.

In Exercises 20–22, find all factors of the number.

20. 16   **21.** 24   **22.** 54

23. One of the theorems of Pierre de Fermat states that every prime number that can be written as a sum of $4n$ and 1, where n is a natural number, can also be written as the sum of two square numbers. For example, when $n = 7$, $29 = 4(7) + 1$ is prime and $29 = 25 + 4$, where 25 and 4 are square numbers. Write the primes less than 100 that can be written as $4n + 1$, where n is a natural number. Then, express each of these primes as the sum of two square numbers.

24. The prime numbers 2 and 3 are consecutive numbers. Can you think of any other pairs of consecutive primes. Explain.

In Exercises 1–6, list the factors of each number. Then find the GCF of the numbers.

1. 12, 30

2. 48, 54

3. 60, 130

4. 108, 198

5. 720, 1200

6. 660, 1155

In Exercises 7–9, write the prime factorization of the numbers. Then find the GCF of the numbers.

7. 88, 121

8. 65, 169

9. 25, 75, 125

In Exercises 10–13, find the GCF of the variable expressions.

10. $2x^2y, 10xy^2$

11. $4x^2y^3, 18xy^2$

12. $5r^2p^3, 20r^3p$

13. $36x^2y^3, 63x^2y^4$

In Exercises 14–16, decide whether the numbers are relatively prime, that is, that their GCF is 1.

14. 256 and 315

15. 321 and 405

16. 190 and 343

In Exercises 17 and 18, determine if the statement is *true* or *false*. Justify your answer.

17. The number 6 is a common factor of 36, 54, and 72.

18. The greatest common factor of $13x^2y^2$ and $27x^2y$ is $13x^2y$.

In Exercises 19–21, find the area and perimeter of the rectangle. Are the two measures relatively prime? Explain.

19.

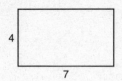

4

7

20.

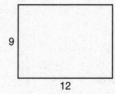

9

12

21.

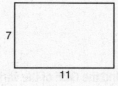

7

11

22. Find the greatest common factor of the terms in the following sequence:
   2, 6, 10, 14, 18, . . .

23. Find the greatest common factor of the terms in the following sequence:
   3, 9, 15, 21, 27, . . .

24. A group of children walk to the corner store and buy cans of soda pop for
   a total of $3.36 and candy bars for a total of $2.45. Each child has one can
   of pop and one candy bar. How many children were in the group? What is
   the cost of one can of soda and one candy bar?

In Exercises 1–6, list the first few multiples of each number. Then use the lists to find the LCM of the numbers.

1. 5, 7   **2.** 3, 8   **3.** 9, 12

4. 12, 14   **5.** 3, 5, 6   **6.** 5, 6, 12

In Exercises 7–10, write the prime factorization of the numbers. Then find their LCM.

7. 36, 54   **8.** 15, 35   **9.** 145, 275   **10.** 81, 216

In Exercises 11 and 12, write the expressions in factored form. Use the results to find the LCM of the expressions.

11. $13xy^2, 26x^2y^3$ **12.** $3x^2, 5y^2$

5.3

Name _____ Date _____

In Exercises 13–16, find all the pairs of numbers that fit the description.

13. Two prime numbers whose LCM is 39.

14. Two composite numbers whose LCM is 36.

15. Two square numbers whose LCM is 100.

16. Two even numbers whose LCM is 72.

17. You have collected empty pop bottles to return for a 8¢ per bottle refund. You want to use the money to buy packs of trading cards for $1.50 per pack. After buying the packs you had no money left over. What is the fewest number of pop bottles you could have returned? How many packs of cards did you buy?

18. Angel's car gets 32 miles per gallon and Mo's car gets 22 miles per gallon. When traveling from Morgan Run to Clinton, they both used a whole number of gallons of gasoline. What is the closest that Morgan Run and Clinton could be? How many gallons did Angel's car use? How many gallons did Mo's car use?

19. Mr. Wilson has a problem. He can't sleep when the dogs in his neighborhood start howling at the full moon. Luckily, it takes the sound of two dogs barking at the same time to awake him. Last night, Sparky started barking at 1:00 A.M. and barked every 12 minutes. Trigger also started at 1:00 A.M. and barked every 14 minutes. After Mr. Wilson fell back to sleep, he woke up again when Sparky and Trigger barked simultaneously. What time was it?

In Exercises 1–6, simplify the fraction.

1. $\dfrac{12}{18}$

2. $\dfrac{8}{36}$

3. $\dfrac{9}{45}$

4. $\dfrac{22}{77}$

5. $\dfrac{4}{38}$

6. $\dfrac{84}{108}$

In Exercises 7–12, simplify the variable expression.

7. $\dfrac{2xy}{6xy^2}$

8. $\dfrac{3ab}{12a^2}$

9. $\dfrac{49z^2}{147z^5}$

10. $\dfrac{16yz^2}{18z}$

11. $\dfrac{24x^3y}{40xy^5}$

12. $\dfrac{38x^2}{95xy^2}$

In Exercises 13–16, graph the fractions on a number line. Then order the fractions from least to greatest.

13. $-\dfrac{3}{8}, -\dfrac{2}{5}, \dfrac{1}{3}, \dfrac{1}{5}$

14. $\dfrac{5}{6}, \dfrac{2}{3}, \dfrac{7}{8}, \dfrac{1}{10}$

15. $-\dfrac{12}{31}, \dfrac{8}{9}, -\dfrac{99}{101}, \dfrac{25}{27}$

16. $-\dfrac{5}{7}, \dfrac{56}{61}, \dfrac{14}{19}, -\dfrac{8}{11}$

In Exercises 17–22, use <, >, or = to complete the statement.

17. $\dfrac{1}{6} \bigcirc \dfrac{1}{9}$

18. $\dfrac{22}{24} \bigcirc \dfrac{33}{36}$

19. $\dfrac{1}{10} \bigcirc \dfrac{3}{18}$

20. $\dfrac{6}{9} \bigcirc \dfrac{8}{12}$

21. $\dfrac{26}{39} \bigcirc \dfrac{5}{8}$

22. $\dfrac{15}{18} \bigcirc \dfrac{65}{78}$

In Exercises 23–25, tell whether the statement is *true* or *false*. Give an example to support your answer.

23. A positive fraction is graphed to the right of zero on a number line.

24. A fraction with a negative numerator whose absolute value is greater than its positive denominator is a number less than -1.

25. A fraction with a positive numerator one greater than its positive denominator is equivalent to $\frac{3}{2}$.

In Exercises 26 and 27, use the table which shows the number of miles ridden per day during a 7 day bike trip from the town of Osceola to the town of Fairview.

Day	1	2	3	4	5	6	7
Number of miles	20	30	30	40	30	40	30

26. Express the number of miles ridden on day 1 as a fraction of the total miles.

27. Express the number of miles ridden on day 6 as a fraction of the total miles.

28. Miss Curtis and Mr. Morgan gave the same test to their eighth grade math classes. In Miss Curtis' class, 21 out of 35 students received a grade of B or higher. In Mr. Morgan's class, 24 out of 36 students received a grade of B or higher. Which class did better? Explain.

In Exercises 1–4, tell whether the number is a member of the given set.

1. -22.2; integers

2. $10.\overline{10}$; rational numbers

3. 1214; whole numbers

4. $\dfrac{27}{13}$; natural numbers

In Exercises 5 and 6, complete the statement using *sometimes, always,* or *never.*

5. A fraction is _____ a rational number.

6. A natural number is _____ a whole number.

In Exercises 7–12, write the fraction as a decimal.

7. $-\dfrac{3}{8}$

8. $\dfrac{5}{22}$

9. $\dfrac{99}{1000}$

10. $\dfrac{23}{9}$

11. $-\dfrac{23}{99}$

12. $\dfrac{76}{75}$

In Exercises 13–18, write the decimal as a fraction. Simplify if possible.

13. 0.7   **14.** 0.52   **15.** 0.95   **16.** 0.22   **17.** $0.\overline{94}$ **18.** $4.\overline{2}$

In Exercises 19–23, tell whether the decimal form of the fraction is *terminating* or *repeating*.

19. $\dfrac{4}{11}$ **20.** $\dfrac{7}{10}$ **21.** $\dfrac{11}{99}$ **22.** $\dfrac{27}{50}$ **23.** $\dfrac{123}{2000}$

24. A group of students participated in a 100 hour rock-a-thon to raise money for a local charity. The table shows the portion of the fund-raiser in which each student was involved. Write each fraction in decimal form. Then order the students from the one which did the most rocking to the least.

Student	Ken	Vicki	Cindy	Jose	Brenda	Doug	JiLynn
Number	$\frac{1}{5}$	$\frac{4}{25}$	$\frac{3}{25}$	$\frac{11}{50}$	$\frac{1}{10}$	$\frac{3}{20}$	$\frac{1}{20}$

In Exercises 1–6, write the fraction as a percent.

1. $\dfrac{2}{20}$ 2. $\dfrac{24}{50}$ 3. $\dfrac{16}{40}$ 4. $\dfrac{39}{60}$ 5. $\dfrac{72}{120}$ 6. $\dfrac{196}{400}$

In Exercises 7–10, find the percent of each figure that is shaded.

7. 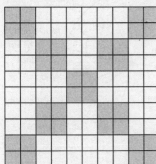   8.    9.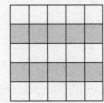

10.

11. Which figure has the least percent of its area shaded? Which figure has the greatest percent of its area shaded?

a.   b.   c.   d.

In Exercises 12–14, find the percent of the letters in the word that are the letter O.

12. CALIFORNIA

13. MONOPOLY

14. ONOMATOPOEIA

In Exercises 15 and 16, the pie graph shows the per person monthly budget for a couple.

15. What is the total budget for the month?

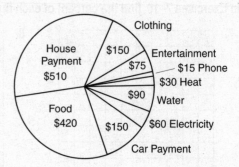

16. Construct a table determining the percent of the budget devoted to each area.

17. Determine which figure does not fit the pattern. Explain.

a.
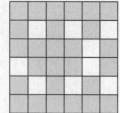

b.
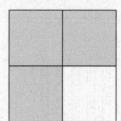

c.
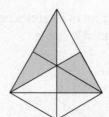

d.
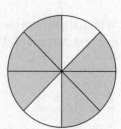

In Exercises 1–6, write the percent as a decimal.

1. 48%   **2.** 16%   **3.** 250%   **4.** 84.2%   **5.** 0.5%   **6.** 38.4%

In Exercises 7–12, write the decimal as a percent.

7. 0.63   **8.** 0.92   **9.** 1.65   **10.** 0.008   **11.** 0.021   **12.** 1.384

In Exercises 13 –18, write the fraction as a percent. Round your answer to the nearest tenth if necessary.

13. $\dfrac{28}{32}$ **14.** $\dfrac{39}{60}$ **15.** $\dfrac{250}{625}$ **16.** $\dfrac{120}{32}$ **17.** $\dfrac{99}{450}$ **18.** $\dfrac{180}{80}$

In Exercises 19–24, write the percent as a fraction. Simplify, if possible.

19. 68%   **20.** 35%   **21.** 79%   **22.** 125%   **23.** 345%   **24.** 105%

In Exercises 25-28, estimate the percent. Then use a calculator to find the exact percent.

25. $\dfrac{99}{200}$ **26.** $\dfrac{28}{63}$ **27.** $\dfrac{234}{144}$ **28.** $\dfrac{99}{50}$

In Exercises 29–31, what percent of the entire region is shaded?

29.

30.

31.

In Exercises 32 and 33, use the following information.

Three hundred people were surveyed and reported that they rearrange furniture in their homes for several reasons. The table shows the data.

Reason	Number of People
Bored with present arrangement	108
Moving to new residence	57
Purchasing new furniture	45
Redecorating	48
Other	42

32. Create a new table showing the percent of the people surveyed who reported each reason. Also include the percent written as a decimal and a fraction in simplest form.

33. Create a bar graph showing the results of the survey.

In Exercises 1–3, find the least and greatest number from each stem-and-leaf plot. Then make an ordered list of the data from the stem-and-leaf plot.

1.

```
3 | 1 4
4 | 2 3 6 8
5 | 0 2 5
6 | 0 1 4 9
7 | 3 6 7
```
7 | 3 represents 73.

2.

```
 7 | 4 5 5 8
 8 | 2 3 9
 9 | 1 4 7
10 | 0 2 8 9 9
11 | 3 5 7 8
```
11 | 3 represents 113.

3.

```
12 | 3 5 6 8 9
13 | 2 3 7 8
14 | 0 4 9
15 | 1 3 3 7 9
16 | 4 5 8
```
16 | 4 represents 16.4.

4. List the two sets of data represented by the double stem-and-leaf plot at the right.

```
        1 | 9
9 8 7 6 | 2 | 0 1
  5 5 3 | 3 | 8 8 9
```
6|2|0 represents 2.6 and 2.0.

5. The following data represents the ages of customers in a restaurant on a particular Saturday between 11:00 A.M. and 1:00 P.M. Organize the data with an ordered stem-and-leaf plot.

```
24  33  39  51  16  18  24  28  33  53
12  13  16  25  35  60  37  27  51  20
32  36  47  41  26  28  17  19  23  39
25  29  34  39  43  51  53  62  60  19
17  23  20  30  33  36  49  42  47  50
```

In Exercise 6, use the set of data below which shows the batting averages of the American League Batting Champions for the years 1970 through 1996.

1970(.329)   1971(.337)   1972(.318)   1973(.350)   1974(.364)   1975(.359)   1976(.333)   1977(.388)

1978(.333)   1979(.333)   1980(.390)   1981(.336)   1982(.332)   1983(.361)   1984(.343)   1985(.368)

1986(.357)   1987(.363)   1988(.366)   1989(.339)   1990(.329)   1991(.341)   1992(.343)   1993(.363)

1994(.359)   1995(.356)   1996(.358)

6. Organize the data in a stem-and-leaf plot.

In Exercises 1 and 2, write an equation for the indicated sum or difference.

1.

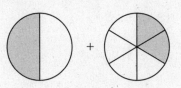

2.

In Exercises 3–20, find the sum or difference. Then simplify, if possible.

3. $\dfrac{3}{7} + \dfrac{2}{7}$

4. $\dfrac{6}{12} - \dfrac{3}{12}$

5. $-\dfrac{7}{15} + \dfrac{2}{15}$

6. $\dfrac{6}{10} - \dfrac{2}{10}$

7. $-\dfrac{8}{3} + \left(-\dfrac{11}{3}\right)$

8. $3\dfrac{1}{3} + 4\dfrac{1}{3}$

9. $\dfrac{7}{9} - \dfrac{2}{3}$

10. $\dfrac{11}{8} + \left(\dfrac{-3}{8}\right)$

11. $1\dfrac{2}{3} + \dfrac{1}{5}$

12. $\dfrac{2}{9} + \dfrac{1}{2}$

13. $\dfrac{-4}{5} - \dfrac{1}{3}$

14. $\dfrac{-3}{10} + \dfrac{3}{4}$

15. $\dfrac{x}{4} + \dfrac{2x}{4}$

16. $\dfrac{3z}{7} - \dfrac{4z}{7}$

17. $-\dfrac{c}{10} + \left(-\dfrac{19c}{10}\right)$

18. $\dfrac{x}{4} + \dfrac{3x}{8}$

19. $\dfrac{a}{3} - \dfrac{11a}{12}$

20. $\dfrac{y}{3} + \dfrac{y}{5}$

21. You are helping to wallpaper your room. You find that for the border you need lengths of 12 ft $10\frac{1}{8}$ in., 10 ft $6\frac{3}{8}$ in., 9 ft $5\frac{5}{8}$ in., and 9 ft $3\frac{7}{8}$ in. What total length (in inches) of border do you need?

22. Suppose on Monday you bought 50 shares of stock at $\$48\frac{1}{8}$ per share. During the week the stocks rose and fell as shown in the table.

Tuesday	Wednesday	Thursday	Friday
Up $\frac{3}{8}$	Up $1\frac{5}{8}$	Down $2\frac{7}{8}$	Up $1\frac{1}{8}$

a. What was the value of the stock on Tuesday?

b. What was the value of the stock on Wednesday?

c. What was the value of the stock at the end of the week?

23. Four friends are working together to paint a barn for one of their uncles. The table gives the fractional part of the job done by each of the four:

Maureen	$\frac{1}{6}$
Hank	$\frac{3}{8}$
Betsy	$\frac{5}{24}$
Carl	$\frac{1}{4}$

a. Who did most of the work?

b. Find the difference in the portions done by Hank and Betsy.

c. Find the portion of the work done by Carl and Maureen.

d. Show that the sum of the four fractions is 1.

In Exercises 1 and 2, use fractions to write an equation for the indicated sum.

1.

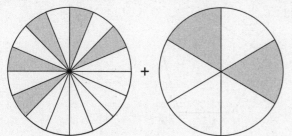

2.

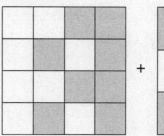

In Exercises 3–8, find the sum or difference. Then simplify, if possible.

3. $\frac{1}{3} + \frac{5}{12}$

4. $\frac{6}{7} - \frac{11}{14}$

5. $-\frac{1}{8} + \left(-\frac{7}{16}\right)$

6. $\frac{1}{3} + \frac{3}{8}$

7. $-\frac{5}{6} + \frac{1}{9}$

8. $\frac{7}{10} + \left(-\frac{2}{3}\right)$

In Exercises 9–11, evaluate the variable expressions when $x = \frac{1}{3}$, $y = \frac{1}{4}$, and $z = \frac{7}{4}$.

9. $x + y - z$

10. $x - y - z$

11. $-x - y + z$

In Exercises 12 and 13, find the perimeter of the figure.

12.

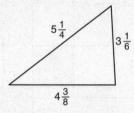

13.

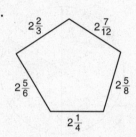

In Exercises 14–16, use the circle graph, which shows the production of energy sources for the United States in 1994.

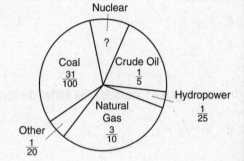

14. Find the sum of the portions for all sources other than nuclear.

15. What portion of production was nuclear power?

16. Find the portion of production that was nuclear power and coal.

In Exercises 1–12, multiply. Then simplify, if possible.

1. $\dfrac{1}{8} \cdot \dfrac{8}{9}$

2. $-\dfrac{3}{7} \cdot \dfrac{21}{25}$

3. $-\dfrac{7}{8} \cdot \dfrac{14}{17}$

4. $3\dfrac{1}{4} \cdot \left(-5\dfrac{3}{5}\right)$

5. $-3\dfrac{1}{7} \cdot \left(-1\dfrac{1}{2}\right)$

6. $\dfrac{3}{8} \cdot \dfrac{-13}{15} \cdot \dfrac{16}{39}$

7. $\dfrac{3x}{4} \cdot 8$

8. $16 \cdot \dfrac{7y}{2}$

9. $-\dfrac{7x}{9} \cdot \dfrac{3}{14x}$

10. $-\dfrac{17t}{20} \cdot \dfrac{24}{51t}$

11. $-\dfrac{7}{8} \cdot \left(\dfrac{-24z}{35}\right)$

12. $-\dfrac{32x}{9} \cdot \dfrac{18}{4}$

In Exercises 13–15, find the area of the figure.

13.

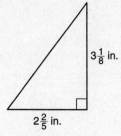

$3\dfrac{1}{8}$ in.

$2\dfrac{2}{5}$ in.

14.

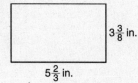

$3\dfrac{3}{8}$ in.

$5\dfrac{2}{3}$ in.

15.

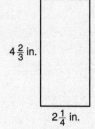

$4\dfrac{2}{3}$ in.

$2\dfrac{1}{4}$ in.

In Exercises 16–19, find the multiplicative inverse.

16. $\dfrac{7}{16}$

17. $-\dfrac{5}{3}$

18. 11

19. $2\dfrac{3}{4}$

20. A farmer wants to plow his land. He owns $7\frac{3}{4}$ acres. It takes about $2\frac{2}{3}$ hours to plow one acre. How long will it take for the farmer to plow his entire farmland?

21. Two hundred shares of stock are purchased at a price of $\$23\frac{5}{8}$ per share and three hundred shares of stock are purchased at $\$86\frac{1}{4}$ per share. Find the total cost of the purchased stock.

Practice

6.4

Name _____ Date _____

In Exercises 1–6, change the percent to a decimal or a fraction. Then multiply.

1. 18% of 800

2. 23% of 120

3. 360% of 8

4. 175% of 40

5. 0.6% of 540

6. 3.5% of 150

In Exercises 7–10, match the percent phrase with the fraction phrase. Then find the percent of the number.

a. $\frac{1}{6}$ of 80

b. $\frac{1}{12}$ of 80

c. $\frac{1}{20}$ of 80

d. $\frac{3}{8}$ of 80

7. 5% of 80

8. 37.5% of 80

9. $16\frac{2}{3}$% of 80

10. $8\frac{1}{3}$% of 80

In Exercises 11–16, use mental math to find the percent of the number.

11. 20% of 25

12. 80% of 20

13. 25% of 8

14. 5% of 40

15. 10% of 150

16. 60% of 500

In Exercises 17–22, estimate. Then multiply to check your estimate.

17. 74% of 55

18. 18% of 39

19. 58.2% of 340

20. 228% of 120

21. 3.05% of 690

22. 101% of 252

In Exercises 23–26, use the rectangle at the right.

23. Find the perimeter and area of the rectangle.

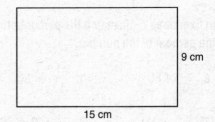

9 cm

15 cm

24. Draw a new rectangle whose dimensions are $33\frac{1}{3}$% of the given rectangle. Find the perimeter and area of the new rectangle.

25. Find $33\frac{1}{3}$% of the perimeter of the given rectangle. Is the result equal to the perimeter of the new rectangle? Why or why not?

26. Find $33\frac{1}{3}$% of the area of the given rectangle. Is the result equal to the area of the new rectangle? Why or why not?

27. There is a sale at the sport store of "20% off." The original price of the new cross-trainers you want is $79.95. What is the sale price?

28. You read in the newspaper that the price of a new CD player is predicted to be 125% of this year's price. If the price of the model you wanted is $525.95, what is the predicted price for next year?

In Exercises 1–21, simplify the expression.

1. $\dfrac{3}{8} \div 2$

2. $\dfrac{3}{8} \div 3$

3. $\dfrac{3}{8} \div 4$

4. $\dfrac{5}{6} \div 2$

5. $\dfrac{5}{6} \div 3$

6. $\dfrac{5}{6} \div 4$

7. $\dfrac{3}{8} \div \dfrac{1}{2}$

8. $\dfrac{3}{8} \div \dfrac{1}{3}$

9. $\dfrac{3}{8} \div \dfrac{1}{4}$

10. $\dfrac{5}{6} \div \dfrac{1}{2}$

11. $\dfrac{5}{6} \div \dfrac{1}{3}$

12. $\dfrac{5}{6} \div \dfrac{1}{4}$

13. $\dfrac{3}{7} \div \dfrac{5}{14}$

14. $6 \div \left(-\dfrac{7}{12}\right)$

15. $-\dfrac{3}{4} \div \dfrac{3}{7}$

16. $\dfrac{16x}{21} \div \dfrac{27x}{12}$

17. $3\dfrac{4}{5} \div z$

18. $p \div 3\dfrac{2}{7}$

19. $\dfrac{5x}{3} \div 3x$

20. $-\dfrac{2}{11} \div \dfrac{y}{33}$

21. $\dfrac{1}{2} \div 2\dfrac{1}{2}$

In Exercises 22 and 23, describe the error. Then correct it.

22.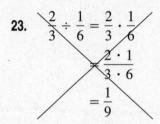

$$10 \div 3\frac{1}{5} = 10 \cdot \frac{16}{5}$$

$$= \frac{10 \cdot 16}{5}$$

$$= 32$$

23.

$$\frac{2}{3} \div \frac{1}{6} = \frac{2}{3} \cdot \frac{1}{6}$$

$$= \frac{2 \cdot 1}{3 \cdot 6}$$

$$= \frac{1}{9}$$

24. A giant size box of washing detergent contains 30 cups. On average, you use $\frac{3}{4}$ cup per load of laundry. How many loads of laundry can you do from this one box?

25. You're having a birthday party for your sister. Thirty people are to attend. You have purchased a 10-foot sub for the party. The sub weighs $8\frac{5}{8}$ ounces per foot. How much does the entire sub weigh? How many ounces does each person receive?

In Exercises 1–15, solve the equation. Check the solution.

1. $2a + \dfrac{3}{5} = 5$

2. $b - \dfrac{1}{6} = \dfrac{2}{3}$

3. $\dfrac{s}{5} - \dfrac{2}{3} = 2$

4. $1\dfrac{1}{3}x = \dfrac{1}{6}$

5. $\dfrac{y}{8} = \dfrac{5}{16}$

6. $2\dfrac{1}{2} = \dfrac{c}{5} + \dfrac{1}{3}$

7. $\dfrac{1}{3}e + \dfrac{3}{2} = 1\dfrac{5}{6}$

8. $\dfrac{4}{5} - w = -\dfrac{3}{10}$

9. $1\dfrac{1}{4} = \dfrac{7}{8}d - \dfrac{3}{4}$

10. $-\dfrac{3}{50} = \dfrac{1}{10} - 3m$

11. $\dfrac{3}{10} + \dfrac{n}{5} = 2$

12. $1\dfrac{3}{8} = \dfrac{a}{4} - \dfrac{3}{16}$

13. $\dfrac{y}{3} + \dfrac{1}{2} = 1\dfrac{1}{6}$

14. $\dfrac{15}{8} = b + \dfrac{3}{32}$

15. $3 = \dfrac{5}{6}c$

In Exercises 16–19, write an equation to solve for _x_. Then solve the equation.

16. Area = $\dfrac{31}{10}$ square units

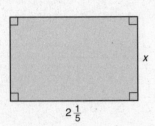

$2\frac{1}{5}$

17. Area = $\dfrac{15}{4}$ square units

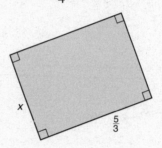

$\frac{5}{3}$

18. Area = $\dfrac{7}{10}$ square units

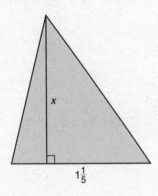

$1\frac{1}{5}$

19. Area = $\dfrac{8}{9}$ square units

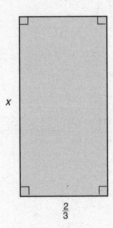

$\frac{2}{3}$

In Exercise 20, write and solve the equation for the sentence.

20. One third of a number minus 6 is 5.

21. Bob can paint the fence alone in 5 hours. Alice can paint the fence alone in $4\frac{1}{2}$ hours. How long will it take them to paint the fence if they work together?

In Exercises 1–12, simplify the expression.

1. $(-3)^2 \cdot (-3)^4$

2. $14^0 \cdot 14^1$

3. $x^{15} \cdot x^{20}$

4. $\dfrac{3^5}{3^2}$

5. $\dfrac{-8^3}{-8^2}$

6. $\dfrac{x^7}{x^3}$

7. $3x^2 \cdot 2x$

8. $\dfrac{(-13)^7}{(-13)^2}$

9. $\left(\dfrac{y}{5}\right)^2 \left(\dfrac{y}{5}\right)^7$

10. $\left(-\dfrac{2}{3}\right)^2 \cdot \left(-\dfrac{2}{3}\right)^3$

11. $\dfrac{-24s^4t}{18s^2}$

12. $\dfrac{6a^5}{54a^2b}$

In Exercises 13 and 14, write and simplify a numerical expression for the given phrase.

13. The product of eight raised to the fifth power and eight raised to the seventh power.

14. The quotient of five raised to the sixth power and five raised to the fourth power.

In Exercise 15–17, simplify and then evaluate the expression.

15. $\dfrac{\left(\frac{4}{7}\right)^7}{\left(\frac{4}{7}\right)^5}$

16. $\dfrac{\left(-\frac{5}{4}\right)^{14}}{\left(-\frac{5}{4}\right)^{11}}$

17. $\dfrac{\left(\frac{1}{2}\right)^6}{\left(\frac{1}{2}\right)^2}$

18. The lengths of the sides of a rectangle are 5^3 yards and 5^2 yards. Write the area of the rectangle as a power of 5.

In Exercises 1–16, simplify the expression.

1. 4^{-3}

2. -3^{-3}

3. $(-2)^4$

4. 100^0

5. $(-8)^0$

6. $(-4)^{-2}$

7. $\left(\dfrac{4}{5}\right)^0$

8. $\left(\dfrac{3}{2}\right)^{-3}$

9. x^{-3}

10. $4y^{-3}$

11. $5z^{-2}$

12. w^0

13. $-5u^{-2}$

14. $-7v^{-5}$

15. $13t^0$

16. $a^{-4}b$

In Exercises 17–24, rewrite the expression using a prime base raised to a negative power.

17. $\dfrac{1}{9}$

18. $-\dfrac{1}{25}$

19. $-\dfrac{1}{5}$

20. $\dfrac{1}{256}$

21. $-\dfrac{x}{121}$

22. $\dfrac{1}{225}$

23. $\dfrac{4}{64}$

24. $-\dfrac{3}{81}$

In Exercises 25–32, rewrite the expression using a negative exponent.

25. $\dfrac{1}{a^5}$ **26.** $\dfrac{1}{b}$ **27.** $\dfrac{1}{-(x^5)}$ **28.** $\dfrac{-1}{y^4}$

29. $\dfrac{3}{a^2}$ **30.** $\dfrac{8}{x^0}$ **31.** $\dfrac{3^2}{x}$ **32.** $\dfrac{7}{y^4}$

33. A nanometer is 10^{-9} meters. A millimeter is 10^{-3} meters. How many nanometers are in a millimeter?

34. Explain whether $2x^{-3}$ and $\dfrac{x^3}{2}$ are multiplicative inverses. Justify your answer.

In Exercises 1–6, write the number in scientific notation.

1. 3500

2. 62,000

3. 0.000375

4. 0.0205

5. 62,153,000

6. 0.0000105

In Exercises 7–12, write the number in decimal form.

7. 3.2×10^5

8. 6.35×10^{-4}

9. 4.3×10^{-3}

10. 9.75×10^4

11. 8.27×10^{-6}

12. 3.25×10^5

In Exercises 13–18, decide whether the number is in scientific notation. If it is not, rewrite the number in scientific notation.

13. 2.5×10^6

14. 0.35×10^6

15. 26.5×10^{-3}

16. 3.2×10^{-6}

17. 764×10^{-3}

18. 5.25×10^{-1}

In Exercises 19–22, evaluate the product. Write the result in scientific notation and in decimal form.

19. $(3.2 \times 10^5)(4 \times 10^2)$

20. $(3.0 \times 10^7)(6.5 \times 10^{-2})$

21. $(5.2 \times 10^{-4})(7.2 \times 10^{-6})$

22. $(9.5 \times 10^3)(2.3 \times 10^{-7})$

In Exercises 23 and 24, decide which is greater. Explain.

23. 1×10^6 or 6×10^5

24. 1×10^{-4} or 4×10^{-3}

25. The star Beta Andromeda is approximately 76 light years from Earth. Estimate the distance to this star if a light year is approximately 5.88×10^{12} miles. Write your estimate in scientific notation.

26. The hydraulic cylinder in a large press contains 2 gallons of oil. When the cylinder is under full pressure the actual volume of oil will decrease by $2(150)(2.0 \times 10^{-5})$ gallons. Write this decrease in decimal and scientific notation. What is the actual volume when the cylinder is under full pressure?

In Exercises 1–3 write the ratio as a fraction $\frac{a}{b}$ in simplest form.

1. 240 feet out of 300 feet
2. 76 out of 144 players
3. 210 hits in 165 games

In Exercises 4–7, write the verbal phrase as a rate or a ratio. Then simplify. Explain why the phrase is a rate or a ratio.

4. Ran 3 miles in 24 minutes
5. 10 out of 60 students agree

6. Rained 2 inches in 40 minutes
7. Painted 2 out of 3 pictures

In Exercises 8–13, express both quantities in a common unit of measure, then write the ratio as a fraction $\frac{a}{b}$ in simplest form.

8. $\dfrac{4 \text{ yards}}{16 \text{ inches}}$

9. $\dfrac{32 \text{ km}}{4000 \text{ m}}$

10. $\dfrac{36 \text{ hours}}{7 \text{ days}}$

11. $\dfrac{7 \text{ pints}}{2 \text{ gallons}}$

12. $\dfrac{3 \text{ feet}}{28 \text{ inches}}$

13. $\dfrac{2 \text{ pounds}}{24 \text{ ounces}}$

14. A family is traveling to the beach for their vacation. At 2 P.M. they stop at a gas station and fill the gas tank. You notice that the odometer reading was 36,525. At 8:30 P.M. they again stop to fill the tank. It takes about 16 gallons to fill. The odometer now reads 36,913.

   a. Determine the number of miles the car travels per gallon of gas.

   b. Determine the average rate, in miles per hour, at which you are traveling during that time period.

In Exercises 15 and 16, decide which is the better buy. Explain your reasoning.

15. a. 2 quarts for $2.15

   b. one gallon for $4.25

16. a. 36 ounce box for $3.72

   b. 3 pound box for $5.36

In Exercises 17 and 18, find the ratio of the perimeter of the shaded figure to the perimeter of the unshaded figure. Then find the ratio of the area of the shaded figure to the area of the unshaded figure.

17.

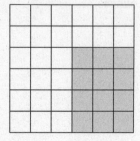

18.

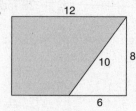

In Exercises 1–9, use the cross products property to solve the proportion.

1. $\dfrac{x}{4} = \dfrac{5}{20}$

2. $\dfrac{4}{5} = \dfrac{a}{30}$

3. $\dfrac{5}{16} = \dfrac{15}{y}$

4. $\dfrac{x}{5} = \dfrac{15}{25}$

5. $\dfrac{6}{11} = \dfrac{w}{22}$

6. $\dfrac{7}{10} = \dfrac{56}{z}$

7. $\dfrac{8}{q} = \dfrac{2}{9}$

8. $\dfrac{10}{35} = \dfrac{2}{p}$

9. $\dfrac{2.5}{y} = \dfrac{5}{12}$

In Exercises 10–15, write the sentence as a proportion. Then solve.

10. x is to 5 as 12 is to 15

11. y is to 12 as 2 is to 3

12. 4 is to 9 as 24 is to z

13. 7 is to 11 as y is to 99

14. 3 is to 4 as w is to 18

15. t is to 10 as 3 is to 35

In Exercises 16–18, use a calculator to solve the proportion. Round your result to the nearest hundredth.

16. $\dfrac{13}{15} = \dfrac{x}{35}$

17. $\dfrac{k}{6} = \dfrac{8}{15}$

18. $\dfrac{25}{32} = \dfrac{m}{18}$

19. The recommended application for a particular type of lawn fertilizer is one 50-pound bag for 575 square feet. How many bags of this type of fertilizer would be required to fertilize 2875 square feet of lawn?

20. One hundred cement blocks are needed to build a wall 16-feet high. How many cement blocks are needed to build a wall 48-feet high?

21. A quality control engineer for a certain buyer found 2 defective parts in a sample of 50. At this rate, what is the expected number of defective parts in a shipment of 50,000.

In Exercises 1–4, the scale of a map is 2 cm to 25 miles. You are given the distance on the map. Find the actual distance.

1. 15 cm   **2.** 7 cm   **3.** 2.2 cm   **4.** 45.6 cm

In Exercises 5 and 6, find the perimeter of the actual object using the scale factor shown on the blueprint.

5.

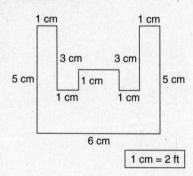

1 cm = 2 ft

6.

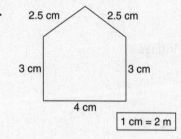

1 cm = 2 m

In Exercises 7–11, use the map of Alaska. The scale factor is
3 cm to 400 miles. Use a centimeter ruler to approximate the
distances between the cities to the nearest 10 miles.

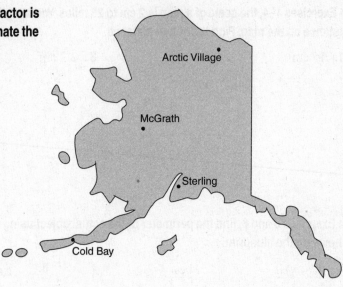

7. McGrath and Arctic Village

8. Sterling and Cold Bay

9. Cold Bay and McGrath

10. Sterling and Arctic Village

11. Cold Bay and Arctic Village

12. You are designing a dog house for the puppy that you received for your
birthday. The scale factor for your design is 0.5 inch to 1 foot. Label the
actual dimensions of the dog house. What is the total surface to be painted
on the house (both ends, sides, and roof)?

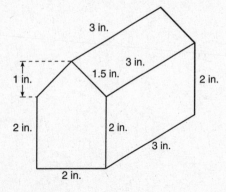

In Exercises 1–4, find the probability of rolling the following number or numbers on a number cube.

1. A six

2. An even number

3. A one or two

4. A number greater than two

In Exercises 5 and 6, consider the following. Six marbles are placed in a bag. One is green, two are yellow, and three are red. Without looking, choose one.

5. What is the probability of choosing a red marble?

6. What is the probability of choosing a yellow marble?

In Exercises 7–10, consider the probability of choosing one card from a standard deck of 52 playing cards. (A face card is a Jack, Queen, or King.)

7. What is the probability of choosing an "8"?

8. What is the probability of choosing a face card?

9. What is the probability of choosing a red face card?

10. What is the probability of choosing a "2" or an Ace?

11. 20 socks are placed in a laundry bag. Use the following statements to determine the number of socks of a particular color.
   • Probability of blue is 0.25.
   • Probability of black is 0.20.
   • Probability of white is 0.50.
   • Probability of argyle is 0.05.

In Exercises 12–14, use the following information.
The number of public school teachers (in thousands)
in the United States in 1995 is shown by region in the
figure.

12. Suppose one teacher is selected at random.
    What is the probability that the teacher is
    located in the

    Pacific: 349   New England: 141

    Mountain: 155   South Atlantic: 385

    West North Central: 202   East South Central: 192

    East North Central: 397   West South Central: 328

    Middle Atlantic: 379

    a. Middle Atlantic Region?

    b. Pacific Region?

13. What is the probability that one teacher
    selected at random is located in one of three
    southern regions?

14. Using only the result from Exercise 13, what
    is the probability that one teacher selected
    at random is *not* located in one of the three
    southern regions?

In Exercises 1–10, write and solve a proportion. Round your answer to the nearest hundredth.

1. 16 is what percent of 500?

2. What is 27 percent of 320?

3. What is 46% of 86?

4. 234 is 36 percent of what number?

5. 27 is 125% of what number?

6. 456 is $33\frac{1}{3}$ % of what number?

7. What is 365% of 430?

8. 2.52 is 18% of what number?

9. 92 is what percent of 86?

10. What is 36% of 125?

In Exercises 11–14, use mental math to solve the equation.

11. 20 is 20% of what number?

12. What is 75% of 400?

13. 6 is what percent of 60?

14. 300 is 200% of what number?

In Exercises 15 and 16, describe and correct the error. Then solve.

15. Problem: 25 is what percent of 675?

Proportion $\dfrac{a}{675} = \dfrac{25}{100}$

16. Problem: What is 52% of 162?

Proportion $\dfrac{100}{162} = \dfrac{p}{52}$

17. A company that manufactures light bulbs states that less than $\frac{2}{5}$% of all light
bulbs manufactured per day are defective. If the company produced 15,000 light
bulbs on a given day how many light bulbs could be expected to be defective?

18. Because of a membership drive for a community center, the current membership
is 125% of what it was a year ago. The membership last year was 7400 members.
How many members does the community center have this year?

19. The annual auto insurance premium for a policyholder is normally $739.
However, after having an automobile accident, the policyholder was
charged an additional 32%. What is the new annual premium?

20. Suppose you buy a motorbike that costs $1450 plus 6% sales tax. Find the
amount of sales tax, and the total bill.

21. A customer left $20 for a meal that cost $16.95. How much was the tip?
What percent of the cost of the meal is the amount of the tip?

22. The monthly salary of an employee is $1000 plus a 7% commission on her
total sales. How much must the employee sell in order to obtain a monthly
salary of $3500?

In Exercises 1–6, find the amount of markup or the amount of discount. Round your answer to the nearest hundredth.

1. $520 surfboard; 20% discount

2. $15 leash; 50% markup

3. $305 wetsuit; 15% off

4. $15 fin; 75% markup

5. $1 wax; 125% markup

6. $14 sunscreen; 25% discount

In Exercises 7–14, find the cost of the item after the markup or discount described. Round your answer to the nearest cent.

7. $45.50 shirt; 20% off

8. $14 compact disc; 25% off

9. $85 shoes; 150% markup

10. $20 concert; 125% markup

11. $345 television; 80% markup

12. $95 jacket; 30% off

13. $65 tire; 15% off

14. $20 textbook; 400% markup

15. A new mountain bike costs 12% more this spring than it did last spring. If the cost of a particular model was $775 last year, what is the increase in price for this year? What is the new price?

16. Your class is trying to raise money to go on a class trip at the end of the school year. The cost of the trip is $2575 for the entire class. The school expects your class to have at least 60% of the money raised by February. How much money will the class have to have by February?

17. A sports store is offering a 40% discount on the style of cross-trainers that you really like. If the regular price is $85.95, how much is the discount? What is the sale price?

18. During the summer you mow lawns and do yard work. Last summer you charged $6.25 per hour. This summer you decide that you will raise your rate 16%. What is the new rate per hour?

19. An advertisement states that a car on sale has been marked down $3167.50. It also states that this was a 15% discount. What was the original list price?

20. A compact disc car stereo was purchased and a 5% sales tax was added. The stereo was $346.29. What was the amount of the sales tax?

Practice	**7.7**

Name _____ Date _____

In Exercises 1–6, find the percent of change.

1. Before: 12 After: 15   **2.** Before: 6 After: 4   **3.** Before: 125 After: 100

4. Before: 150 After: 175   **5.** Before: 200 After: 150   **6.** Before: 320 After: 336

In Exercises 7–10, decide whether the change is an increase or a decrease and find the percent of change.

7. November: $1.18
   December: $1.20

8. Opening day: $18.20
   Closing day: $16.80

9. Monday: $324.00
   Friday: $365.00

10. Beginning balance: $5002.00
   Ending balance: $4890.00

In Exercises 11–14, use a percent to describe the pattern. Then find the next three numbers.

11. 2, 8, 32, 128, ? , ? , ?   **12.** 640, 320, 160, 80, ? , ? , ?

13. 1, 10, 100, 1000, ? , ? , ?   **14.** 15625, 6250, 2500, 1000, ? , ? , ?

In Exercises 15–18, decide whether the statement is true or false. Explain your reasoning.

15. Three times a number is a 300% increase of the number.

16. One third a number is a $66\frac{2}{3}\%$ decrease of the number.

17. A 90% decrease of 60 is 54.

18. A 20% increase of 80 is 96.

In Exercises 19 and 20, describe a real-life situation that involves the given decrease or increase.

19. A 100% increase

20. A decrease of 15%

21. Copy and complete the table.

Original Number	New Number	Percent Change
55	?	20% increase
55	?	20% decrease
?	350	75% increase
?	350	75% decrease
60	75	?
60	45	?

22. In 1990, the number of tropical storms and hurricanes reaching the United States coastline was 14. In 1993, the number was 8. Find the percent decrease from 1990 to 1993.

23. In 1920, the life expectancy at birth for a man in the United States was 53.6 years. By 1993, it had increased to 72.1 years. Find the percent increase from 1920 to 1993.

In Exercises 1–8, find the simple interest and the balance of the account.

1. $1250 at 4% for 3 months

2. $800 at 8% for 1 year

3. $500 at 10% for 6 months

4. $1100 at 5% for 9 months

5. $3000 at 6% for 1 month

6. $400 at 6% for 2 months

7. $1500 at 7% for 5 months

8. $1,000,000 at 4.5% for 1 year

In Exercises 9–14, find the simple interest rate.

9. $67.50 interest on $4500 for 3 months

10. $2125 interest on $85,000 for 4 months

11. $35 interest on $1200 for 7 months

12. $315 interest on $3500 for 1 year

13. $1760 interest on $32,000 for 6 months

14. $127.50 interest on $1700 for 9 months

15. You deposit $9000 in a savings account. Determine what interest rate you would have to get to earn $540 in interest for 1 year.

16. You deposit $3500 in a savings account. Determine how long it would take to earn $70 while earning 8% simple interest.

In Exercises 17 and 18, use the following information.

Your brother wants to borrow $8500 to buy a used car. Your mother will lend him the money at 8% simple interest for 6 years. Your grandfather will lend him the money at 11% simple interest for 4 years.

17. What is the amount of interest that he would pay to your mother? to your grandfather?

18. From which relative should your brother borrow the money? Explain.

1. How many times in 3 years is interest added to your account if interest is compounded monthly? quarterly? semiannually? annually?

In Exercises 2–5, use the information to find the balance in an account when $14,000 is invested for one year.

2. 5% compounded semiannually

3. 7.5% compounded annually

4. 3.5% compounded quarterly

5. 4% compounded monthly

In Exercises 6 and 7, use the following information.

You deposit $1500 into a savings account for five years. The bank is offering an annual interest rate of 7% compounded quarterly.

6. Determine how many compounding periods occur in five years.

7. Use the formula for compound interest to find the balance in your account at the end of five years.

In Exercises 8–10, use the information to find the amount in the account after the given number of years.

8. Principal: $4000;
   annual interest rate: 7%
   semiannually for 2 years

9. Principal: $700;
   annual interest rate: 10%
   quarterly for 5 years

10. Principal: $1000;
    annual interest rate: 11%
    monthly for 5 years

11. Your friend invests $1000 in a savings account at 10% annual interest compounded semiannually. You invest $1000 in another account at 10% annual interest compounded quarterly. At the end of three years, determine who will have more money in savings.

In Exercises 1–6, use the diagram at the right.

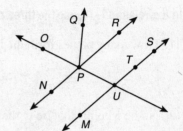

1. Name 3 different line segments that lie on $\overleftrightarrow{OU}$.

2. Name 5 rays that have beginning point P.

3. Name 2 pairs of lines that intersect.

4. Name 2 lines that appear parallel.

5. Name a ray in the opposite direction of $\overrightarrow{PO}$.

6. What is another name for the line segment $\overline{PR}$?

In Exercises 7–10, use the diagram at the right to decide whether the given symbol is a line, a line segment, a ray, or the length of a line segment.

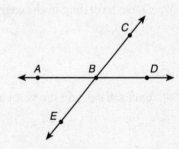

7. $\overrightarrow{BE}$ 8. $\overleftrightarrow{BC}$ 9. BD 10. $\overline{AB}$

In Exercises 11–14, use the three-dimensional figure at the right.

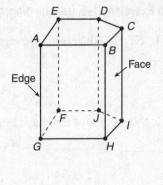

11. How many planes form the figure's faces?

12. Name 5 points that lie in the same plane.

13. Name 3 lines that appear parallel to $\overleftrightarrow{AB}$.

14. Name 3 rays that have the beginning point *I*.

In Exercises 15 and 16, draw the indicated figure.

15. 3 lines, 2 of which do not intersect

16. 4 lines that intersect in one point

In Exercises 17– 19, use the drawing of the lion cage.

17. Does the ceiling of the cage appear to be parallel to the floor of the cage?

18. On each side, do the vertical steel bars appear parallel?

19. What would you consider each side of the cage to be, in terms of the words of geometry?

Practice

8.2

Name _____ Date _____

Use a protractor to measure the angle. Tell whether the angle is acute, obtuse, right, or straight.

1.

2.

3.

In Exercises 4–11, use a protractor to draw an angle with the given measure.

4. 80°   **5.** 10°   **6.** 75°   **7.** 40°

8. 150°   **9.** 100°   **10.** 25°   **11.** 51°

In Exercises 12–15, use the figure at the right.

12. List the acute angles.   **13.** List the obtuse angles.

14. List the right angles.   **15.** List all angles with vertex *W*.

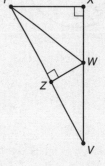

Find the measure of the angle that is complementary to an angle with the given measure.

16. 25°   **17.** 85°   **18.** 45°

Find the measure of the angle that is supplementary to an angle with the given measure.

19. 25°   **20.** 150°   **21.** 90°

In Exercises 22 and 23, measure and name angles formed by the clock hands.

22.

23.

In Exercises 1–5, use the figure at the right.

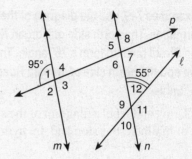

1. Which two lines are parallel?

2. Is ∠12 congruent to ∠8? Why or why not?

3. List all angles whose measure is 55°.

4. List all angles whose measure is 85°.

5. Name two corresponding angles that have the same measure.

6. Explain why the indicated angles are congruent.

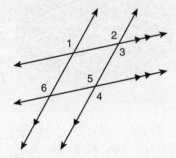

In Exercises 7–9, use the diagram of the city streets and the information. The north side of Morgan Road and the east side of Ryan Street meet to form a 75° angle. The west side of Danver Drive and the north side of Morgan Road meet to form a 105° angle.

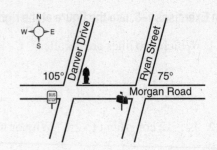

7. Draw and label a diagram of the streets. Identify the location of mailbox, bus stop and fire hydrant.

8. Present a case to explain why Danver Drive and Ryan Street are parallel.

9. Find measures of the angles (or intersection) at which the mailbox, bus stop, and fire hydrant are placed.

10. Chef Carlo Vincento wishes to decorate his world famous strawberry pie with fresh strawberries. He wishes to place these strawberries at the intersections of the parallel lines of whipped cream. However, for cosmetic appearances, the strawberries are only to be placed at congruent angles to the initial strawberry. Place a dot at every congruent angle to the one marked on the figure.

In Exercises 1–3, classify the triangle by its angles and by its sides.

1.

2.
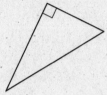

3.
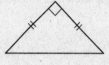

In Exercises 4–6, sketch a triangle that is an example of the indicated type. Then label it with appropriate angles measures and congruence tick marks.

4. Right scalene

5. Obtuse scalene

6. Acute isosceles

In Exercises 7–10, complete the statement with *always, sometimes,* or *never.*

7. An isosceles triangle is __?__ a right triangle.

8. An obtuse triangle is __?__ a right triangle.

9. A right triangle is __?__ an equilateral triangle.

10. A right triangle is __?__ an isosceles triangle.

In Exercises 11–13, classify the quadrilateral from its appearance. Use the name that best describes the quadrilateral.

11.

12.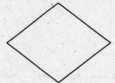

13.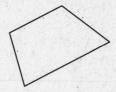

In Exercises 14 and 15, complete the statement with *always*, *sometimes*, or *never*. Explain your reasoning.

14. A rectangle is __?__ a square.

15. A parallelogram is __?__ a trapezoid.

In Exercises 16 and 17, find the values of *x* and *y*.

16. Rectangle

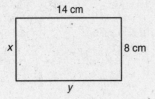

17. Rhombus

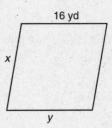

Decide whether the figures are congruent. If they are, write a congruence statement. Then list the corresponding angles and the corresponding sides.

1.

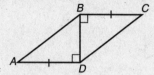

In Exercise 2, find the indicated angle measures and side length.

2.

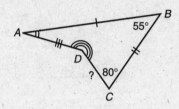

3. Which of the following polygons are regular?

a.

b.

c.

In Exercises 4–6, match the quadrilateral with a congruent quadrilateral.

a.

b.

c.

4.

5.

6.

In Exercises 7–10, use the regular octagon shown at the right.

7. What is the measure of $\angle D$?

8. What is the length of EF?

9. Find the perimeter of the octagon.

10. What is the sum of the measures of the angles of a regular octagon?

Name _____ Date _____

In Exercises 1–4, find the area of the polygons.

1.

18
12

2.

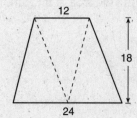

12
18
24

3.

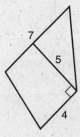

7
5
4

4.

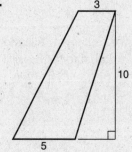

3
10
5

In Exercises 5 and 6, make a sketch on graph paper to represent the "equation."
Then write a formula for the area of the final figure.

5. (2 Congruent Right Triangles) + (2 Congruent Isosceles Triangles) = (1 Rectangle)

6. (2 Isosceles Trapezoids) + (2 Congruent Isosceles Triangles) = (1 Parallelogram)

7. The garage roof shown is made from two isosceles trapezoids and two isosceles triangles. Find the area of the entire roof.

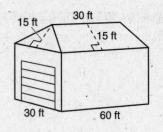

8. You are mowing your lawn, as shown. The mower cuts a path 18 inches wide. If you cut 48 paths parallel to the base, what is the area of the lawn which you have cut?

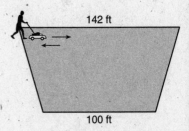

9. You are repairing a large replica of the HOLLYWOOD sign in California. The plans for the "D" are shown. Each square represents 1 square foot. Find the area of the letter.

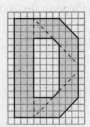

Decide whether the shaded figure is a reflection of the unshaded figure in line ℓ.
If not, sketch the reflection of the unshaded figure in line ℓ.

1.

2.

3.

In Exercises 4–6, draw the reflection of the figure in line ℓ.

4.

5.

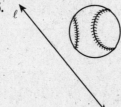

6.

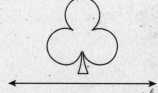

8.7

Name _____ Date _____

In Exercises 7–11, consider the coordinates X(−3, 4), Y(−1, 2), and Z(−4, 1) of △XYZ. Find the coordinates of the image after the indicated reflection(s).

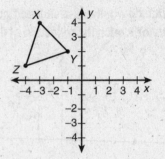

7. Reflect about the x-axis

8. Reflect about the y-axis

9. Reflect about the x-axis, then about the y-axis

10. Reflect about the y-axis, then about the x-axis

11. Reflect about the y-axis, then again about the y-axis

12. Which letters of the alphabet look like the same letter when reflected about a vertical line? List them.

13. Use a mirror to decode the secret message.
    "TOH OOT HTOUM YM MOM HO"

In Exercises 1–3, write a verbal description of the transformation that maps the unshaded figure to the shaded figure.

1.
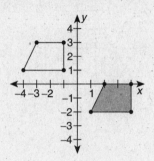

2.
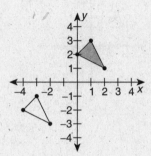

3.
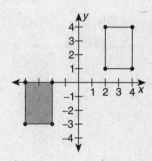

In Exercises 4 and 5, you are given the coordinates of a figure. Draw the figure in a coordinate plane. Then draw its image after the indicated translation. Use coordinate notation to describe the translation

4. $A(2, 3)$, $B(4, -1)$, $C(-4, 0)$;
    5 units down and 1 unit left

5. $J(-2, 4)$, $K(2, 4)$, $L(4, 7)$, $M(-4, 7)$;
    2 units right and 4 units down

8.8

In Exercises 6–8, match each diagram with one of the translations below.

a. 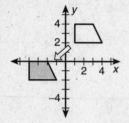   **b.** 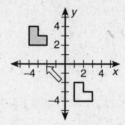   **c.**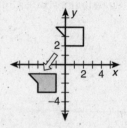

6. $(x - 5, y + 6)$ **7.** $(x - 3, y - 5)$ **8.** $(x - 5, y - 4)$

9. Find the name of Carl's dog. The dog's name has five letters. Given are the four ordered pairs that enable you to find the pup's name. Start at (1, 1) on the grid and write down each letter you land on according to the transformation.

1. Start at (1, 1)
2. $(x + 3, y + 7)$
3. $(x - 2, y - 4)$
4. $(x + 5, y - 2)$
5. $(x + 2, y + 7)$

<table>
<tr><td>

Practice

</td><td>

8.9

</td><td>Name</td><td>Date</td></tr>
</table>

In Exercises 1–3, you are given a pair of similar figures. Solve for x.

1.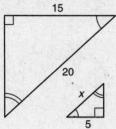

2.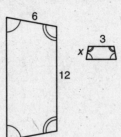

3.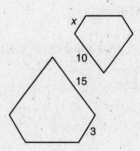

4. Which two figures are similar?

a.

b.

c.

d.

In Exercises 5–8, trapezoids *ABCD* and *JKLM* are similar, as shown at the right.

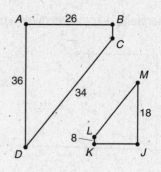

5. Write four equal ratios for *ABCD* and *JKLM*.

6. Find the scale factor of *ABCD* to *JKLM*.

7. Find the following:
   a. *BC*   b. *ML*   c. *KJ*

8. $m\angle C = m\angle$ ⬚ ?

9. You have purchased a scale model of an off-road vehicle. The scale factor is 1 to 24. The model is 2.9 in. high, 2.75 in. wide, and 6.4 in. long. Find the height, width, and length, in feet, of the actual vehicle.

10. The map of the lake area below is drawn with a scale factor of 1 in. to 40 feet. Find the greatest distance across the lake.

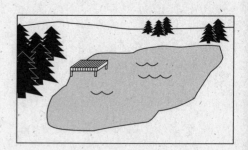

In Exercises 1–6, write the two square roots of the number.

1. 36

2. 12

3. 1.96

4. 0.64

5. 400

6. $\frac{25}{36}$

Use a calculator to estimate the square root. Round your answer to the nearest tenth

7. $\sqrt{28}$

8. $\sqrt{5682}$

9. $\sqrt{0.69}$

10. $\sqrt{500}$

11. $\sqrt{65.5}$

12. $\sqrt{3721}$

13. $\sqrt{286}$

14. $\sqrt{15}$

In Exercises 15–17, use the given area of the shaded square to estimate the length of one of its sides. Use the grid to check your answer. The small squares in the grid are each 1 square unit.

15.
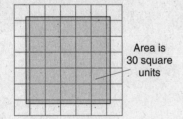
Area is 30 square units

16.
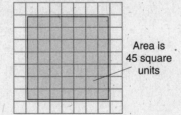
Area is 45 square units

17.
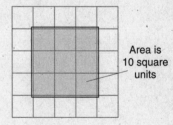
Area is 10 square units

Without using a calculator, estimate the square roots of the number. Give your answers to the nearest tenth.

18. 35   **19.** 10   **20.** 5   **21.** 50

The area of a square is given. Estimate the length of one side of the square. Round your answer to the nearest tenth.

22. 22 square miles   **23.** 65 square feet

24. 13 square millimeters   **25.** 112 square inches

Solve the equation using mental math.

26. $a^2 = 121$ **27.** $\dfrac{25}{9} = x^2$ **28.** $y^2 = 8100$

9.2

In Exercises 1–5, match each number with a point on the number line.

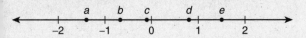

1. $-\sqrt{0.01}$ 　　　　**2.** $-\sqrt{\frac{4}{9}}$ 　　　　**3.** $-\sqrt{1.96}$ 　　　　**4.** $\sqrt{2.25}$ 　　　　**5.** $\dfrac{\sqrt{16}}{5}$

In Exercises 6–9, complete the statement using *always, sometimes,* or *never*. Explain your answer.

6. A rational number is ___?___ an integer.

7. A square root of a number is ___?___ a rational number.

8. An integer is ___?___ an irrational number.

9. A rational number is ___?___ a real number.

In Exercises 10–15, graph the numbers on a number line. Use a calculator if needed. Then complete the statement using <, >, or =.

10. $\sqrt{2} \bigcirc \dfrac{7}{5}$ 　　　　**11.** $-\sqrt{\dfrac{9}{25}} \bigcirc -\dfrac{14}{25}$ 　　　　**12.** $\dfrac{9.6}{0.6} \bigcirc \sqrt{2.56}$

13. $\sqrt{\dfrac{25}{36}} \bigcirc \sqrt{\dfrac{64}{81}}$ 　　　　**14.** $-\sqrt{10} \bigcirc -\dfrac{81}{25}$ 　　　　**15.** $\dfrac{\sqrt{625}}{9} \bigcirc \dfrac{14}{5}$

In Exercises 16 and 17, put the numbers in order from least to greatest.

16. $5.11, \dfrac{26}{5}, \sqrt{26}, 5$

17. $9, \sqrt{82}, \dfrac{80}{9}, \sqrt{80}$

In Exercises 18–23, determine whether the number is rational or irrational.
Explain your reasoning.

18. $\frac{13}{2}$

19. $-\frac{41}{19}$

20. $\sqrt{12}$

21. $-\sqrt{16}$

22. $-\sqrt{8}$

23. $\sqrt{\frac{9}{4}}$

In Exercises 1–3, find the length of the hypotenuse.

1.

2.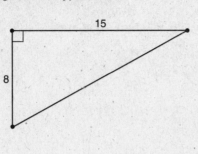

3.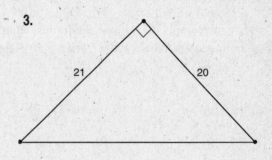

The length of a leg of an isosceles right triangle is given. Find the length of the hypotenuse.

4. 4   **5.** 15.3   **6.** 0.45

In Exercises 7–9, use the Pythagorean Theorem to solve the right triangle.

7.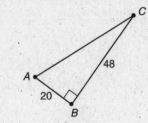

8.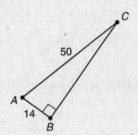

9.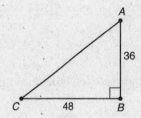

10. The instruction booklet for a 40 foot ladder states: When leaning against a vertical wall, the base of the ladder should be between 10 and 18 feet from the wall. Under those conditions, what are the maximum and minimum heights that the ladder will reach on the wall?

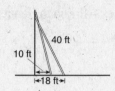

11. A baseball diamond is a perfect square. The distance between the bases is 90 feet. A base runner is on first and attempts to steal second. If the catcher is 3 feet behind home plate, how far must he throw the ball to reach second base?

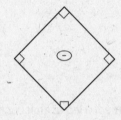

12. Due to road construction, a stretch of highway has to be closed. The detour runs 11 miles west and 13 miles south as shown. About how many miles of highway are closed?

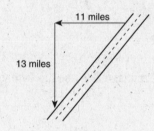

13. A radio station broadcast tower is anchored by four wires each 160 feet from the base of the tower. Each of those wires is 240 feet long. Find the height of the tower.

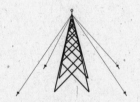

Determine whether the triangle with the given side lengths is a right triangle.

1. 10, 24, 26   2. 2.0, 2.1, 2.9   3. 14, 48, 50

Copy and complete the table. Determine whether a triangle with side lengths
a, b,* and *c* is a *right triangle,* an *acute triangle,* or an *obtuse triangle.

	a	b	c	$a^2 + b^2$	c^2	Type of triangle
4.	4	12	13			
5.	5	12	13			
6.	6	12	13			
7.	5	13	14			

8. You are mounting an 8 foot TV antenna on your flat garage roof. The installation kit provides three cables each 10 feet in length that attach to the top of the antenna. How far should each of these cables be placed from the base of the antenna so that the antenna remains vertical?

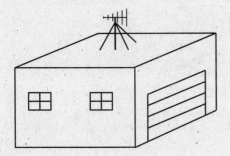

9. A plane flies in a straight line to Jacksonville. It is 100 miles east and 150 miles north of the point of departure, Osceola. How far did the plane fly?

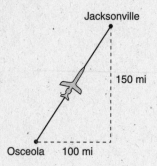

Jacksonville

150 mi

Osceola   100 mi

10. The flagpole shown below is 40 feet long. It is supported by a wire that is 46 feet long that is secured 20 feet from the base of the flagpole. Is the flagpole vertical?

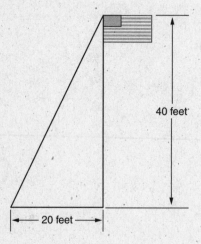

40 feet

20 feet

In Exercises 1–3, use the graph to estimate the distance between the points. Then use the distance formula to find the actual distance between the points. Compare your estimate and the actual distance between the points.

1.

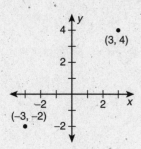

2.

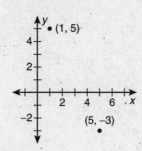

3.

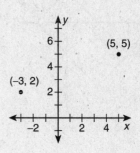

The expression represents the distance between two points. Give possible coordinates for the points.

4. $\sqrt{(1 - (-1))^2 + (-3 - 5)^2}$

5. $\sqrt{(-2 - 3)^2 + (-7)^2}$

Find the length and the midpoint of $\overline{AB}$ given the coordinates of the points. If necessary, round your answer to the nearest tenth.

6. $A(5, 1)$ and $B(-2, 7)$

7. $A(0, -3)$ and $B(5, -1)$

8. $A(-4, -1)$ and $B(0, 6)$

9. $A(7, 8)$ and $B(-9, -9)$

In Exercise 10, show that parallelogram *WXYZ* is a rectangle by showing that its diagonals are equal in length.

10.

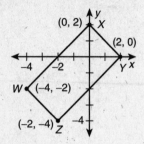

11. The map at the right is being used to plan a 26.3 mile marathon. Coordinates are given in miles. The locations of the participating towns on the map are: Curtis (0, 0), Clearfield (10, 2), Buster (5, 7), and Angel City (1, 4).

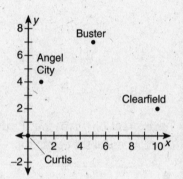

Which of the following planned routes is nearest to the 26.3 mile requirement?

a. Curtis to Clearfield to Angel City to Curtis

b. Curtis to Clearfield to Buster to Angel City to Curtis

c. Curtis to Buster to Clearfield to Curtis

d. Curtis to Buster to Angel City to Clearfield to Curtis

Middle School Mathematics, Course 2

In Exercises 1–6, write the inequality represented by the graph.

1.
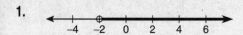

2.
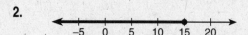

3.
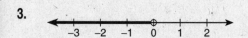

4.

5.

6.

In Exercises 7–10, write the two inequalities for the phrase. Then graph the inequalities.

7. All real numbers less than $\sqrt{10}$.

8. All real numbers greater than $\sqrt{11}$.

9. All real numbers greater than or equal to $-\sqrt{5}$.

10. All real numbers less than or equal to $-\sqrt{15}$.

In Exercises 11–16, graph the inequality.

11. $x \le 3$

12. $x < 0$

13. $x \ge -10$

14. $x < -3$

15. $x > 9$

16. $x \ge 4$

In Exercises 17–22, solve the inequality. Then graph the solution.

17. $w + 4 \ge 3$

18. $x - 4 < -2$

19. $y + 5 < 2$

20. $r - 10 \le 4$

21. $-2 < t + 6$

22. $16 < x + 9$

In Exercises 23–25, write an equivalent inequality. Then write the inequality verbally.

23. $x \geq 5$ **24.** $t \leq -10$ **25.** $w > -4$

In Exercises 26–29, write an algebraic model for the verbal phrase. Then solve.

26. q plus 12 is less than -4. **27.** z minus 10 is less than or equal to 5.

28. The difference of p and 16 is greater than -12. **29.** 42 is greater than or equal to the sum of t and 22.

In Exercises 30–33, write an algebraic model for the verbal model.

30. Vicki is at least 13 years old. Let a represent Vicki's age.

31. Mo hit more than 18 home runs this season. Let h represent the number of homers.

32. The temperatures never rose above $-5°F$ yesterday. Let t represent the temperature.

33. You should study more than 2 hours per day. Let h represent the number of hours.

In Exercises 34 and 35, write a real-life situation that can be represented by the graph.

34.

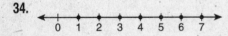

35.

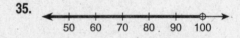

In Exercises 1 and 2, describe and correct the error.

1.
$$5x \leq -32$$
$$\tfrac{1}{5} \cdot 5x \geq \tfrac{1}{5} \cdot (-32)$$
$$x \geq -\tfrac{32}{5}$$

2.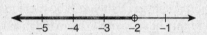
$$-\tfrac{1}{2}z > -5$$
$$-2 \cdot \left(-\tfrac{1}{2}z\right) > -2 \cdot (-5)$$
$$z > 10$$

In Exercises 3–6, match the inequality with the graph of it's solution.

a.

b.

c.

d.

3. $-\tfrac{1}{3}z < -4$ **4.** $6x < -12$ **5.** $\tfrac{1}{4} \geq -\tfrac{1}{16}z$ **6.** $0.3w \leq -1.8$

In Exercises 7–18, solve the inequality. Then graph the solution.

7. $5n < 12$ **8.** $-3m < 11$ **9.** $\tfrac{x}{4} \geq 6$ **10.** $25 \geq 15k$

11. $\tfrac{3}{8} < -4c$ **12.** $-\tfrac{3}{4} \leq \tfrac{5}{4}w$ **13.** $-\tfrac{2}{5}p \leq 10$ **14.** $19 \geq -6m$

15. $15 < 0.4p$ **16.** $\tfrac{a}{12} < -6$ **17.** $14d < -21$ **18.** $-3.2w < 1.28$

19. You are recycling aluminum cans to save enough money to buy a new portable CD player which costs $120.75. The recycling center is paying 35¢ per pound of aluminum. How many pounds of aluminum cans do you need to recycle to have at least $120.75?

20. You and your family are traveling to the mountains for a weekend vacation. The last sign you saw said that your destination is still 255 miles away. Your parents say that you'll be there in at most $4\frac{1}{2}$ hours. How fast will your family have to travel to arrive in at most $4\frac{1}{2}$ hours?

21. Your family has added a new room to your home. You've budgeted $450 for carpeting. The room has a floor area of 30 square yards. What is the most you can spend per square yard so that the cost of the carpeting is not more than $450?

22. You're taping some of your favorite singles onto a 90 minute blank cassette. On average each of your favorite singles is 4 minutes 30 seconds long. What is the greatest number of singles that can be recorded without cutting any song short?

In Exercises 1 and 2, describe the error. Then correct it.

1.
$$-3x - 2 \leq 5$$
$$-3x - 2 + 2 \leq 5 + 2$$
$$\frac{-3x}{-3} \leq \frac{7}{-3}$$
$$x \leq -\frac{7}{3}$$

2.
$$5(3y + 2) > -3$$
$$15y + 10 > -3$$
$$15y + 10 - 10 < -3 - 10$$
$$15y < -13$$
$$y < -\frac{13}{15}$$

In Exercises 3–6, match the inequality with its solution.

a. $x < 5$ **b.** $x < -5$ **c.** $x > -5$ **d.** $x > 5$

3. $3(x + 3) < -6$ **4.** $2(10x - 1) < 4x + 6(x + 8)$

5. $3x + 1 > -7(x + 7)$ **6.** $\frac{4}{5}x > 3\left(\frac{1}{5}x - 1\right) + 4$

In Exercises 7–14, solve the inequality. Then graph the solution.

7. $1 - 2b < 3b - 4$ **8.** $2x + 5 > 7(4 - x)$ **9.** $7x + 2 < -19$ **10.** $\frac{1}{9}z + 11 \geq -9$

11. $2a + 7 < -5a + 28$ **12.** $\frac{3}{8}x \leq \frac{1}{8}x + 10$ **13.** $8(x - 3) \geq 2x + 6$ **14.** $-3x + 19 > -5x$

In Exercises 15–17, let $2n$, $2n + 2$, and $2n + 4$ be three consecutive even integers. Write the inequality that represents the verbal sentence. Then solve the inequality.

15. The sum of three consecutive even integers is less than or equal to 18.

16. The sum of three consecutive even integers is more than 66.

17. The sum of three consecutive even integers is less than -12.

In Exercises 18 and 19, find the possible values of x.

18. The perimeter of the rectangle is at most 36 square centimeters.

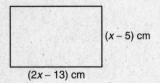

(x – 5) cm

(2x – 13) cm

19. The area of the triangle is more than 40 square feet.

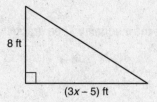

8 ft

(3x – 5) ft

20. Suppose you are taking a class in which the grade is based on six 100-point exams. To earn an A in the course, you must have a total of at least 90% of the points. Your scores on the first five exams are 85, 92, 88, 96, and 87, respectively. How many points do you have to obtain on the sixth exam to earn an A in the course?

In Exercises 1–5, use the box-and-whisker plot. There are 20 numbers in the collection, and each number is different.

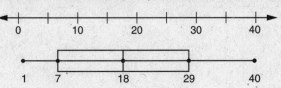

1. Name the least and greatest numbers.

2. Name the first, second, and third quartiles.

3. What percent of the numbers are less than 29?

4. What percent of the numbers are greater than 29?

5. What percent of the numbers are between 18 and 40?

6. Draw a box-and-whisker plot for the data.
   4, 33, 99, 20, 79, 95, 22, 35, 93, 10, 54, 85, 97, 27, 12, 5, 72, 1, 42, 30

In Exercises 7 and 8, use the box and whisker plot which shows the average monthly high temperature distribution for Milwaukee, Wisconsin in degrees fahrenheit.

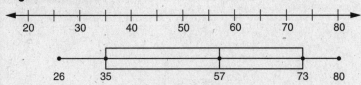

7. Write a description of Milwaukee's average monthly high temperature.

8. Create a box-and-whisker plot for Honolulu's average monthly high temperature in which the lowest monthly average high temperature is 80° F, the highest is 88° F, the first quartile is 81° F, the median is 84.5° F, and the third quartile is 87° F.

In Exercises 9 and 10, use the data which lists the scores of Super Bowl winning teams and Super Bowl losing teams.

Winners: 35, 33, 16, 23, 16, 24, 14, 24, 16, 21, 32, 27, 35, 31, 27, 26, 27, 38, 38, 46, 39, 42, 20, 55, 20, 37, 52, 30, 49, 27, 35

Losers: 10, 14, 7, 7, 13, 3, 7, 7, 6, 17, 14, 10, 31, 19, 10, 21, 17, 9, 16, 10, 20, 10, 16, 10, 19, 24, 17, 13, 26, 17, 21

9. Using the same scale, create a box-and-whisker plot for both scores.

10. What do the plots tell you about the winning and losing scores? Write your answers in paragraph form.

In Exercises 1–4, find the circumference and area of the figure. Use 3.14 for π. Round your result to the nearest tenth.

1.

$r = 6.1$ in.

2.

$d = 2.2$ in.

3.

$d = 2.8$ ft

4.

$r = 14.2$ in.

In Exercises 5 and 6, find the radius and diameter of the figure. Use 3.14 for π. Round your result to the nearest tenth.

5.

$A = 735.0$ in.^{2}

6.

$C = 57.8$ cm

In Exercises 7 and 8, find the area of the shaded portion of the figure. Use 3.14 for π. Round your result to the nearest tenth.

7.

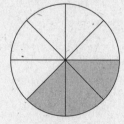

$r = 5$ cm

8.

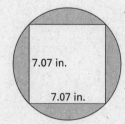

7.07 in.

7.07 in.

$d = 10$ in.

In Exercises 9 and 10, use the following information and the diagram. The shape of the outfield fence in a baseball stadium is that of a quarter circle. The distance from home plate to the wall is 330 feet. Use 3.14 for π.

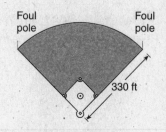

9. What is the length of the circular wall from foul pole to foul pole?

10. What is the area of the entire playing field?

In Exercises 11 and 12, use the following information and the diagram. The center yellow bull's eye has a radius of 2 inches. The ratio of the outer circle's radius to the middle circle's radius to the yellow circle's radius is 5 to 3 to 1. Use 3.14 for π.

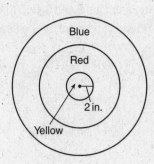

11. Find the radius of the middle circle and the outer circle.

12. Find the area of each colored area.

In Exercises 1–4, use the figure on the right.

1. Name a pair of coplaner lines.

2. Name a pair of skew lines.

3. Is the plane containing points
   A, E, F, and *G* parallel to the plane
   containing points *B, C, H* and *I*?

4. Is the plane containing points
   A, B, C, D, and *E* parallel to the plane
   containing points *F, G, H I,* and *J*?

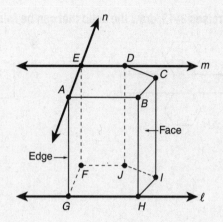

In Exercises 5–7, give the mathematical name of the solid.

5.

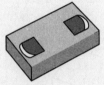

6.

7.

In Exercises 8–13, draw the solid that can be folded from the net.

8.

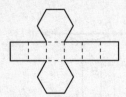

9.

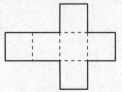

10.

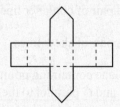

11.

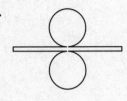

12.

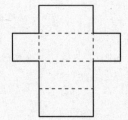

13.

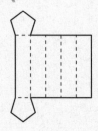

14. Use the figure shown which represents a barn.

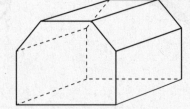

   a. How many faces does the barn have?

   b. How many vertices does the barn have?

   c. How many edges does the barn have?

In Exercises 1–6, find the surface area of the right prism or right cylinder.
Use 3.14 for π. Round your results to the nearest tenth.

1.

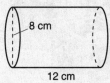

8 cm

12 cm

2.

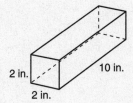

2 in.

2 in.

10 in.

3.

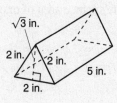

$\sqrt{3}$ in.

2 in.

2 in.

2 in.

5 in.

4.

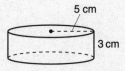

5 cm

3 cm

5.

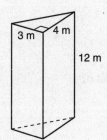

3 m   4 m

12 m

6.

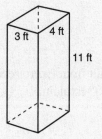

3 ft   4 ft

11 ft

7. Perform the following steps to find the surface area of the solid.
Use 3.14 for π. Round your results to the nearest tenth.

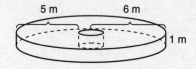

5 m   6 m

1 m

Step 1: Find the area of a base (the area of the larger circle minus the
area of the smaller circle).

Step 2: Find the area of the outside lateral surface (the diameter of the
large circle times π times the height).

Step 3: Find the area of the inside lateral surface (the diameter of the
small circle times π times the height).

Step 4: Add the areas. (Remember to add 2 bases.)

In Exercises 8–11, use the blocks at the right. Each block is
3 inches by 3 inches by 3 inches.

8. Find the surface area of one cube.

9. Imagine that the blocks are placed side by side to spell APE.
   Find the surface area of the new solid.

10. Is the result from Exercise 9 three times the result of
    Exercise 8? Explain.

11. Find the surface area if the blocks spell PEA.

12. Find the surface area of a nickel. For best results find the
    surface area in millimeters.

Find the volume of the prism. (The solids in Exercises 2 and 3 are right prisms.)

1.

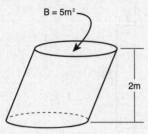

B = 5m²

2m

2.

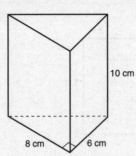

10 cm

8 cm   6 cm

3.

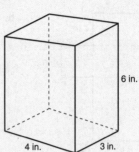

6 in.

4 in.   3 in.

In Exercises 4–6, find the missing measure of the right prism given the volume V.
(In Exercises 4 and 6 the prism has a rectangular base.)

4.

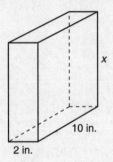

x

10 in.

2 in.

$V = 320 \text{ in.}^3$

5.

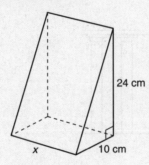

24 cm

x   10 cm

$V = 2160 \text{ cm}^3$

6.

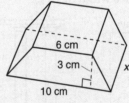

6 cm

3 cm   x

10 cm

$V = 240 \text{ cm}^3$

In Exercises 7–9, draw the prism formed by the net. Then find its volume.

7.
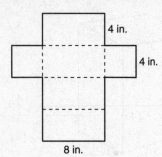
4 in.

4 in.

8 in.

8.
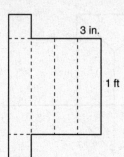
3 in.

1 ft

9.
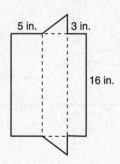
5 in.   3 in.

16 in.

10. How much plaster of paris is needed to make four miniature pillars for a model of a home if the pillars are square based prisms with a height of 12 in. and face width of 2 in.?

Base of pillar

2 in.

2 in.

In Exercises 1–4, find the volume of the cylinder.

1.
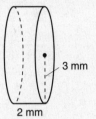
3 mm

2 mm

2.
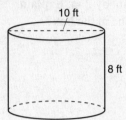
10 ft

8 ft

3.
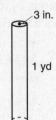
3 in.

1 yd

4.
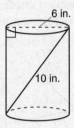
6 in.

10 in.

In Exercises 5–8, find the radius of the base or the height.

5.
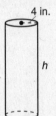
4 in.

h

$V = 1105.08$ in.^{3}

6.
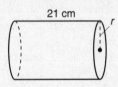
21 cm

r

$V = 3231.06$ cm^3

7.
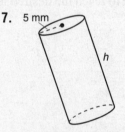
5 mm

h

$V = 1491.5$ mm^3

8.
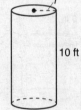
r

10 ft

$V = 196.25$ ft^3

9. Find the dimensions and volume of the largest cylinder that can be packed inside a box that has dimensions 14 in. by 7 in. by 2 in. Explain your reasoning. How much extra space would there be in the box?

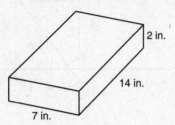

2 in.

14 in.

7 in.

10. A cylindrical fish tank 24 inches high has a base with a radius of 8 inches. You are filling the tank with water to a height of 22 inches. If the water is being pumped in at a rate of 2 cubic inches per second, how many minutes will it take to reach the desired level?

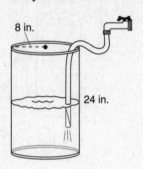

8 in.

24 in.

11. Find the volume of the solid below.

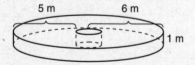

5 m   6 m

1 m

In Exercises 1–4, find the volume of the solid. Use 3.14 for π. Round your results to the nearest tenth.

1.

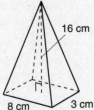

16 cm
8 cm   3 cm

2.

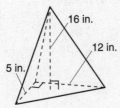

16 in.
12 in.
5 in.

3.

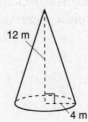

12 m
4 m

4.

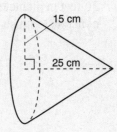

15 cm
25 cm

In Exercises 5 and 6, draw each solid and find its volume. Use 3.14 for π.

5. Pyramid with base 5 cm by 5 cm and height 3 cm

6. Cone with base radius 3 in. and height 4 in.

In Exercises 7–9, find the volume of the solid. Use 3.14 for π. Round your result to the nearest tenth.

7.

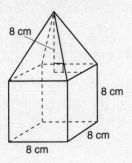

8 cm
8 cm
8 cm
8 cm

8.

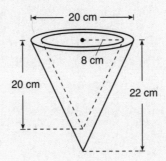

20 cm
8 cm
20 cm
22 cm

9.

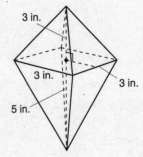

3 in.
3 in.
3 in.
5 in.

10. To complete a construction job, a contractor needs 145 more cubic yards of concrete. If there is a cone-shaped pile of concrete mix measuring 36 feet in diameter and 12 ft high on the job site, is there enough concrete to finish the job? Explain your result.

11. A jeweler is casting small gold cones for a special piece of jewelry. She has 60 g total of gold to use and wishes to make twelve cones with a radius of 0.5 cm and a height of 1 cm. If gold weighs 19.32 grams per cubic centimeter, does she have enough gold to make the cones? Explain.

10.7

Name _____ Date _____

In Exercises 1–4, find the volume of the sphere. Use 3.14 for π. Round results to the nearest tenth.

1.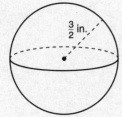
$\frac{3}{2}$ in.

2.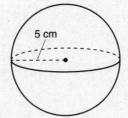
5 cm

3.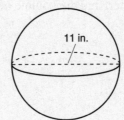
11 in.

4.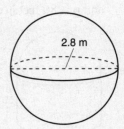
2.8 m

5. Approximate the volume of each planet shown in the table. Write the results in scientific notation.

Planet	Diameter (in miles)	Volume (in mi³)
Earth	7,926	
Mercury	3,030	
Venus	7,520	
Mars	4,217	
Jupiter	88,700	
Saturn	74,975	
Uranus	32,200	
Neptune	30,800	
Pluto	1,423	

6. How many minutes will it take you to inflate a giant beach ball with a radius of 32 inches using an electric pump that can inflate at a rate of 60 in.³/sec?

7. A grain storage tank shown below in the shape of a cylinder covered by a half sphere called a hemisphere. If the height of the cylinder is 50 feet and it is 80 feet in diameter, find the volume of the tank.

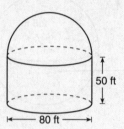

50 ft

80 ft

8. How much extra space will you have inside a box 44 cm by 44 cm by 44 cm after placing a bowling ball with a radius of 21.8 cm in it?

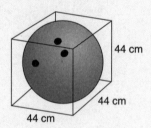

44 cm

44 cm

44 cm

In Exercises 9–11, complete the table. Leave your answers in terms of π.

	Radius of sphere	Diameter of sphere	Circumference of sphere at its "equator"	Volume of sphere
9.	10 mm	?	?	?
10.	?	?	36π in.	?
11.	?	?	?	$\frac{500}{3}\pi$ yd^3

1. Match the solid with the similar solid.

A.

24 m

10 m

B.

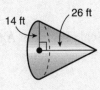

14 ft   26 ft

C.

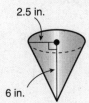

2.5 in.

6 in.

D.

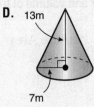

13m

7m

In Exercises 2 and 3, the solids shown are similar. Use the ratio of their surface areas to find the ratio of their volumes.

2.

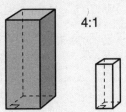

4:1

3.

4:9

    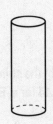

In Exercises 4–7, use the scale factor (of the given solid to a similar solid) to find
the surface area and volume of the similar solid.

		Surface Area	Volume	Scale Factor of A to B
4.	Solid A	64 in.²	28 in.³	1:2
	Solid B	?	?	
5.	Solid A	?	?	2:1
	Solid B	608π in.²	1920π in.³	
6.	Solid A	36 cm²	12 cm³	?
	Solid B	324 cm²	?	
7.	Solid A	108 ft²	54 ft³	2:3
	Solid B	?	?	

In Exercises 8–10, find the volume of the solid. Then use the scale factor to find
the volume of a similar solid. Use 3.14 for π. Round to the nearest hundredth.

8.

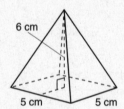

6 cm

5 cm   5 cm

9.

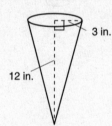

3 in.

12 in.

10.

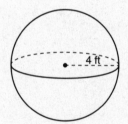

4 ft

In Exercises 1–4, copy and complete the table for each function.

1. $y = \dfrac{x}{3}$

Input, x	0	?	15
Output, y	?	2	?

2. $y = x - 10$

Input, x	0	2	4
Output, y	?	?	?

3. $y = 6x$

Input, x	1	3	5
Output, y	?	?	?

4. $y = 3 + 2x$

Input, x	?	?	11
Output, y	1	3	?

In Exercises 5 and 6, use the graph at the right. It shows the number of feet, that a mountain climber has traveled up the side of a 300 foot cliff after climbing for _t_ hours.

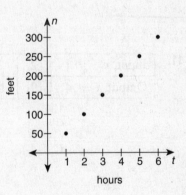

5. Make a table of the input _t_ and the output _n_.

6. Write a function rule that represents the number of feet climbed in _t_ hours.

In Exercises 7 and 8, use the following information. You are joining a video rental club, MOO-V's. They charge an annual fee of $5 plus $1.50 per movie.

7. Make a table of the cost c for one year of renting n movies. Use input values of 10, 20, 30, 40, and 50 movies.

8. Write a function rule that represents the cost of renting n movies for one year.

In Exercises 9–12, write a function rule that relates x and y.

9.

Input, x	1	2	3	4	5	6
Output, y	1	3	5	7	9	11

10.

Input, x	1	2	3	4	5	6
Output, y	2	1	0	−1	−2	−3

11.

Input, x	1	2	3	4	5	6
Output, y	4	9	14	19	24	29

12.

Input, x	1	2	3	4	5	6
Output, y	1.5	2	2.5	3	3.5	4

In Exercises 1–3, decide whether the ordered pair is a solution of $2x - 3y = 4$.

1. $(-1, -2)$ **2.** $(5, -2)$ **3.** $(7, \frac{10}{3})$

In Exercises 4–6, copy and complete the table of values below to show solutions of the given equation.

4. $x - y = 4$ **5.** $y = 3x - 2$ **6.** $2x + y = 5$

x	-3	-2	-1	0	1	2	3
y	?	?	?	?	?	?	?

In Exercises 7 and 8, translate the sentence as an equation. Then write the equation in function form.

7. The sum of 3 times a number and half another number is 10.

8. The difference of a number and 4 times another number is -12.

In Exercises 9–11, match the linear equation with the figure. Write the linear equation in function form and list several solutions.

a.

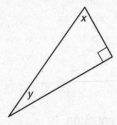

b.

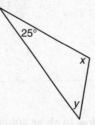

c.

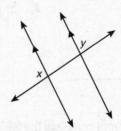

9. $x + y = 155$

10. $x + y = 180$

11. $x + y = 90$

In Exercises 12–14, use the following information.

For the years 1980 through 1994, a small college's enrollment can be modeled by the linear equation $N = 1500 + 60t$, where N is the enrollment and t is the number of years after 1980.

12. Determine the enrollment in 1987.

13. Determine the enrollment in 1994.

14. How many more students were enrolled each successive year?

In Exercises 15 and 16, copy and complete the table. Then describe the pattern and write a rule for the function.

Input, x	1	2	3	4	5	6
Output, y	?	?	?	?	?	?

15. You are finding the perimeter of a rectangle with width x and length 12 units.

16. You have a younger sister named Ginger. Ginger is in the xth grade and you are 4 years ahead of her.

In Exercises 1–3, match each equation with its graph.

a.

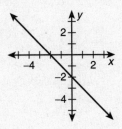

b.

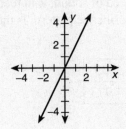

c.

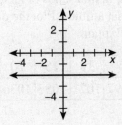

1. $y = 2x$

2. $y = -x - 2$

3. $y = -2$

In Exercises 4–7, graph the equation.

4. $y = 2x + 1$ **5.** $y = 3x - 2$ **6.** $x = -1$ **7.** $y = \frac{1}{4}x$

8. The point $(2, 8)$ lies on the graph of $y = cx + 2$. What is the value of c?

9. The point $(-2, 4)$ lies on the graph of $y = cx - 8$. What is the value of c?

10. The speed of sound decreases as the altitude increases. Given in the table is the altitude, h, in thousands of feet, and the speed of sound, v, in feet per second, at that altitude. Plot the data and describe the pattern. Is the pattern linear? Explain.

h	0	5	10	15	20	24	30	35
v	1116	1097	1077	1057	1036	1015	995	973

In Exercises 11–13 use the following information.

A one-day car rental costs $20 plus $.10 per mile.
The function $C = 20 + 0.1m$, models the situation.

11. Explain what C and m represent in the function.

12. Copy and complete the table of values. Graph the ordered pairs from the table.

m	0	20	40	60	80
C	?	?	?	?	?

13. Use your graph to estimate the cost of the car rental if the car is driven 50 miles.

In Exercises 1–3, graph the equation and find the intercepts of the graph.

1. $x - 4y = 3$

2. $7x - 2y = 60$

3. $5y = 20 - 3x$

In Exercises 4–6, identify the intercepts of the graph.

4.

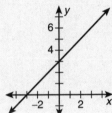

5.

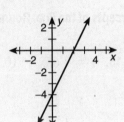

6.

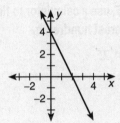

In Exercises 7–10, match the equation with its graph. (Finding the intercepts of the graph may be helpful.)

a.

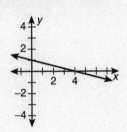

b.

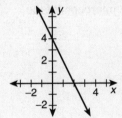

c.

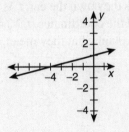

d.

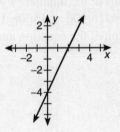

7. $2x + y = 4$

8. $2x - y = 4$

9. $y = \frac{1}{4}x + 1$

10. $y = -\frac{1}{4}x + 1$

In Exercises 11–13, find the intercepts of the graph of the equation and use them to sketch a quick graph. Check your graph by finding and plotting a third solution.

11. $y = -2x + 10$ **12.** $x - y = 3$ **13.** $x + \frac{1}{2}y = 4$

In Exercises 14 and 15, use a calculator to find the intercepts of the line. Round your results to the nearest hundredth.

14. $y = -2.15x + 4.25$ **15.** $y = 3.65x - 10.25$

16. The relationship between Fahrenheit temperature, F, and Celsius temperature, C, is given by the linear equation, $F = \frac{9}{5}C + 32$. Find the coordinates (C, F) of the intercepts of the graph and explain what they mean.

17. Your parents purchase a new automobile for $16,500. The value of the car depreciates linearly (at a constant rate). The value, V, of the car in terms of the number of years they own the car, t, is given by the equation, $V = 16,500 - 1500t$. Find the coordinates (t, V) of the intercepts of the graph of the equation and explain what they mean.

In Exercises 1 and 2, the slopes of four lines are listed. Determine which slope is the steepest of the lines.

1. $m = 3, m = \frac{7}{2}, m = 4, m = \frac{11}{3}$

2. $m = -6, m = -\frac{1}{2}, m = -4, m = 0$

In Exercises 3–5, find the slope of the line.

3.
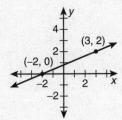

4.
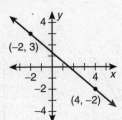

5.
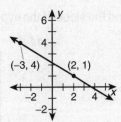

In Exercises 6–9, plot the points. Then find the slope of the line through the points.

6. $(2, 6), (-3, 4)$

7. $(0, 4), (-3, 0)$

8. $(-1, -2), (-3, -2)$

9. $(0, -6), (-2, -1)$

11.5

Name _____   Date _____

In Exercises 10–12, find the slope. Assume a left-to-right orientation.

10.

210 ft

630 ft

11.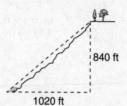

840 ft

1020 ft

12.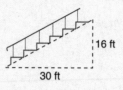

16 ft

30 ft

In Exercises 13–18, find the slope of the hypotenuse.

13.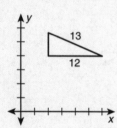

13

12

14.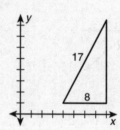

17

8

15.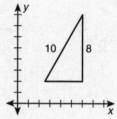

10   8

16.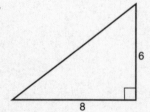

6

8

17.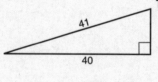

41

40

18.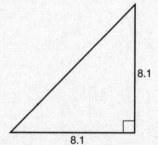

8.1

8.1

11.6

In Exercises 1–4, match the equation with its graph.

a. 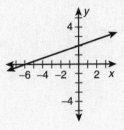 b. 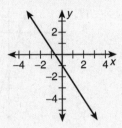 c. 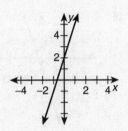 d.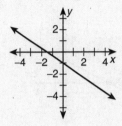

1. $y = 3x + 2$ **2.** $y = \frac{1}{3}x + 2$ **3.** $y = -\frac{2}{3}x - 1$ **4.** $y = -\frac{3}{2}x - 1$

In Exercises 5– 10, find the slope and y-intercept of the line whose equation is given. Then sketch a quick graph of the line.

5. $y = 2x + 4$ **6.** $y = -\frac{1}{2}x + 2$ **7.** $y = 3x - 2$

8. $8y = -32x + 56$ **9.** $3x + 30y = 0$ **10.** $6x + 3y = 27$

In Exercises 11–14, decide whether the statement is true or false. Explain.

11. The line $3x - 9y = 12$ has a slope of 3 and a y-intercept of 4.

12. The line $10y = 2x - 70$ has a slope of $\frac{1}{5}$ and a y-intercept of -7.

13. The line $3x + 2y - 6 = 0$ rises to the right.

14. The line $6y = 2x$ rises to the right and passes through the origin.

In Exercises 15–17, write the equation of the line.

15.
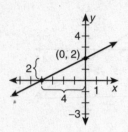

16.
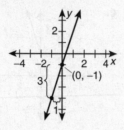

17.
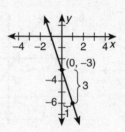

In Exercises 18–20, use the following information.

For 1990 through 1994, the per capita consumption of chicken, C, in
pounds, in the U.S. increased at a rate that was approximately linear. This
relationship can be modeled by $C = 1.79t + 42.76$, where t is the number of
years after 1990.

18. What is the slope and y-intercept of the consumption model?

19. How much more chicken was consumed each year?

20. Sketch a quick graph of the model.

1. Given in the table are the number of practice hours per week of 8 different golfers and their score on a par 72 golf course. Use a scatter plot to estimate the score of a golfer who practices 9 hours a week.

Golfer	1	2	3	4	5	6	7	8
Hours	2	4	5	6	8	10	5	7
Scores	90	85	80	78	72	67	82	76

2. Given in the table is the actual air temperature and the wind-chill factor at a wind speed of 10 mph. Use a scatter plot to estimate the wind-chill factor at an actual air temperature of 20°F and 10°F.

Actual Temperature	35°F	25°F	15°F	5°F	0°F	−5°F	−15°F
Wind Chill Factor	22°F	10°F	−3°F	−15°F	−22°F	−27°F	−40°F

3. Each time you get dimes or quarters for change, you throw them into a jar. You have saved $50 in order to buy three new CD's that you want.

   a. Write a verbal and algebraic model to represent the total saved.

   b. Create a table of values and graph the model.

   c. Interpret the intercepts of the graph in a real-life context.

4. A salesperson receives a 3% commission on sporting goods sold at a sale
price and a 4% commission on sporting goods sold at the regular price.
The salesperson earned a $250 commission.

   a. Write a verbal and an algebraic model to represent the total earned.

   b. Create a table of values and graph the model.

   c. Interpret the intercepts of the graph in a real-life context.

5. The winning times for the men's 100 meter freestyle in the Olympic Games
for 1948–1996 are shown in the graph.

   a. What does this graph tell you about the winning times during
   this 48 year period?

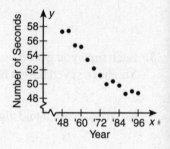

   b. Describe the pattern. If this pattern were to continue, what would
   be the winning time in 2000?

   c. Do you think this pattern can continue for another 48 years? Explain.

In Exercises 1–6, determine whether the ordered pair is a solution of the inequality. Explain your answer.

1. $3x + y \geq 12, (4, 0)$

2. $5x - 6y < 30, (8, -1)$

3. $10x - 24y \leq 120, (6, -5)$

4. $y \leq -3x + 18, (7, -5)$

5. $y \geq 2x - 10, (12, 16)$

6. $2x - 8y > 16, \left(10, \frac{1}{4}\right)$

In Exercises 7–9, match the inequality with its graph.

a.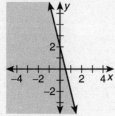

b.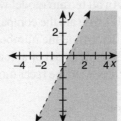

c.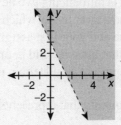

7. $y < 2x - 1$

8. $3y + 6x > 9$

9. $4x + y \leq 2$

In Exercises 10–12, graph the inequality. Then list several solutions.

10. $y \geq -\frac{1}{2}x + 4$

11. $y < -3x + 1$

12. $y \leq -3$

In Exercises 13–16, write an algebraic inequality that represents the statement.

13. The sum of the number of boys and twice the number of girls is less than 45.

14. The perimeter of a rectangular garden cannot exceed 400 feet.

15. The difference between the number of CD's and cassettes that you own is at least 42.

16. Joey and Paul of Joey and Paul's Painting have over 70 years of combined experience.

17. A bike company is introducing two new models. An all terrain model which sells for $625, and a racer model which sells for $500. You are the company's newest employee and your first assignment is to determine the number of models of each that must be sold in order to reach a sales goal of at least $25,000. Let a represent the all terrain model and r represent the racer model.

a. Write the inequality that represents the situation.

b. Graph the inequality.

c. List three solutions of the inequality.

In Exercises 18 – 20, write an inequality whose solutions are given by the graph.

18.
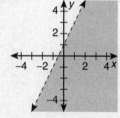

19.
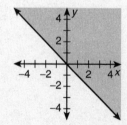

20.
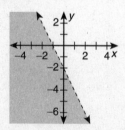

Write a system of linear equations that represents the conditions.

1. y is 5 less than x, *and* y is one fourth of x.

2. The sum of a number x and one third another number y is 12, *and* y is 2 less than x.

Graph the system of equations. Then find the solution.

3. $y = x + 1$
   $y = 2x - 1$

4. $2y = x - 1$
   $y = x$

5. $3x + y = 8$
   $y = 2x + 1$

Write a system of inequalities that represents the conditions.

6. The difference of two numbers x and y is less than 5, *and* 2 more than y is less than x.

7. The sum of a number x and 4 less than three times another number y is less than 43 *and* y is greater than half of x.

Graph the system of inequalities.

8. $y > x - 2$
$y < -2$

9. $y + 2 \geq x$
$x + y > 2$

10. $y + 2x \leq 3$
$x > y - 2$

Write a system of linear equations. Then graph the system and find the solution.

11. The difference of 9 and a number y is one third another number x, *and* the sum of x and y is 4.

12. The sum of two numbers x and y is 14, *and* x is 3 less than three times y.

Write a system of linear inequalities. Then graph the system.

13. The difference of two numbers x and y is greater than -5, *and* one half x is greater than y.

14. The sum of three times a number x and another number y is less than 7, *and* y is less than x.

15. The difference of two numbers x and y is less than 4, *and* the sum of x and twice y is less than 10.

Simplify the expression.

1. $(4x)^3$ **2.** $(5x)^2$ **3.** $(-3y)^4$ **4.** $(-2z)^5$

5. $(de)^3$ **6.** $(-fg)^3$ **7.** $-(fg)^3$ **8.** $-(fg)^4$

Evaluate the power. Write your answer in scientific notation.

9. $\left(5 \times 10^2\right)^2$ **10.** $\left(3 \times 10^5\right)^3$ **11.** $\left(3 \times 10^0\right)^3$ **12.** $\left(3 \times 10^5\right)^0$

13. $\left(4.2 \times 10^3\right)^2$ **14.** $\left(2.5 \times 10^5\right)^3$ **15.** $\left(3.3 \times 10^9\right)^2$ **16.** $\left(1.6 \times 10^6\right)^4$

Simplify the expression.

17. $(5xy)^2$ **18.** $5(xy)^2$ **19.** $5(xy)^3$ **20.** $(5xy)^3$

21. $(-5xy)^2$ **22.** $5(-xy)^2$ **23.** $5(-xy)^3$ **24.** $(-5xy)^3$

25. $-(5xy)^2$ **26.** $-(-5xy)^2$ **27.** $-5(-xy)^3$ **28.** $-(5xy)^3$

Simplify the expression.

29. $\left(\dfrac{x}{2}\right)^2$ **30.** $\left(\dfrac{y}{2}\right)^3$ **31.** $\left(\dfrac{3}{z}\right)^4$ **32.** $\left(\dfrac{1}{z}\right)^7$

33. $\left(\dfrac{4a}{b}\right)^2$ **34.** $\left(\dfrac{a}{3b}\right)^3$ **35.** $\left(\dfrac{-a}{3b}\right)^3$ **36.** $\left(\dfrac{a}{-3b}\right)^2$

Simplify the expression.

37. $\left(x^4\right)^2$ **38.** $\left(x^2\right)^4$ **39.** $\left(a^3b^4\right)^5$ **40.** $\left(-cd^2\right)^3$

41. A cube has sides of length $\dfrac{x}{2}$. Find its volume in terms of x.

12.2 Name _____ Date _____

In Exercises 1–3, determine whether the expression is a polynomial. If it is, state whether it is a monomial, a binomial, or a trinomial.

1. $\sqrt{3}x^3 - 2x + 4$

2. $\frac{1}{2}x^2 - 4.2x$

3. $6x - \frac{2}{x^3} + 11$

In Exercises 4–9, write the polynomial in standard form. Then list its terms.

4. $3z - 2z^3 + 14z^2$

5. $6x^4 - 2x + \frac{1}{2}x^2$

6. $10 - 2y - 3y^3$

7. $8 - 3u^3 - u^5$

8. $\frac{5}{3}v + 2v^3 - 1 - 8v^2$

9. $0.2w + 1.3w^3 + 6 - 2.7w^2$

In Exercises 10–15, simplify the polynomial and write the result in standard form.

10. $3x - 2x^2 + 7x$

11. $z^4 - 3z^2 + z - 4z^2$

12. $5 - 4x^2 + 6 - 11x^2$

13. $\frac{4}{5}m^2 - 6 + 3m^2 - 11$

14. $5a + 2a^2 + a + a^4$

15. $3b^2 - 4b^3 - 7b^2 - b^3$

In Exercises 16–19, use the following information.

As of 1993, the world's tallest building was in Chicago. Its construction was completed in 1974. It is 110 stories high and measures 1454 feet in height. A penny is dropped from the top and its height, h, after t seconds is given by the equation $h = -16t^2 + 1454$.

16. Complete the table.

t	1	2	3	4	5	6	7	8	9	10
h										

17. What is the penny's height after 6 seconds?

18. When will the penny hit the ground?

19. If the penny was thrown upward with a velocity of 20 ft/sec, the equation to model its height would be $h = -16t^2 + 20t + 1454$. Find its height after 10 seconds and 11 seconds. Explain your results.

In Exercises 1 and 2, add or subtract the polynomials using a horizontal format
State the degree of the result.

1. $(-3x^2 + 4x - 7) + (8x^2 - 3x - 3)$

2. $(-k^3 - 2k + 1) - (3k^2 - 4k - 11)$

In Exercises 3–6, add the polynomials using a vertical format.

3.
$$\begin{array}{r} w^3 - 3w^2 + 8w - 11 \\ + \quad 3w^3 + 2w^2 - 10w - 7 \\ \hline \end{array}$$

4.
$$\begin{array}{r} 3d^4 - 3d^3 + 2d^2 - 16d - 11 \\ + \quad -5d^4 + 2d^3 - 11d^2 - 10d - 7 \\ \hline \end{array}$$

5.
$$\begin{array}{r} 3x^3 - 2x^2 + 5x - 11 \\ -(-3x^3 + 11x^2 - 7x - 6) \\ \hline \end{array}$$

6.
$$\begin{array}{r} 2y^4 - 11y^3 - 2y^2 + 5y - 11 \\ - (-y^4 + 6y^3 + 11y^2 - 7y + 10) \\ \hline \end{array}$$

In Exercises 7 and 8, describe and correct the error.

7.
$$\begin{array}{r} -4x^3 + 2x^2 \qquad\quad -4 \\ + \qquad - 3x^3 + 2x + 8 \\ \hline -4x^3 - x^2 + 2x + 4 \end{array}$$

8.
$$\begin{array}{r} 3x^3 + 2x^2 - 6x + 7 \\ -(2x^3 - 6x^2 - 4x - 8) \\ \hline x^3 - 4x^2 - 10x - 1 \end{array}$$

In Exercises 9 and 10, find the perimeter of the polygon. Then evaluate the
perimeter when $x = 8$.

9.

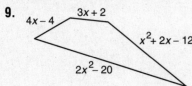

10.

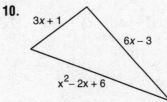

In Exercises 11 and 12, find an expression that represents the area of the unshaded region. Then evaluate the area when $x = 3$.

11.

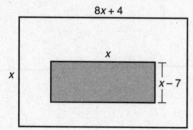

12.

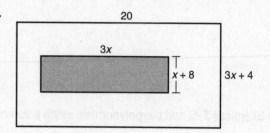

In Exercises 13–16, perform the indicated operations.

13. $(3x^2 - 7x + 5) + (-4x^2 - 6x + 11) + (x^2 - 3x + 7)$

14. $(-5k^2 - 11k + 10) + (3k^2 - 7k + 11) - (7k^2 - 4k + 3)$

15. $(-w^2 + 5) - (w^2 - 11w + 2) + (3w^2 - 11)$

16. $(4x^3 - 7x + 2) - (x^2 - 4x + 6) - (3x^3 - 2x^2 + 7x + 5)$

In Exercises 1–9, find the product.

1. $3x(4x^2 - 2)$

2. $-t^2(3t^3 + 2t - 3)$

3. $6w(w^4 - 3w^2 - 1)$

4. $12c^2(-c^2 + 2)$

5. $-3x(2x^3 - 2x^2 + 4x - 5)$

6. $-n^3(n^4 - 3n^3 + 2n^2 - 6)$

7. $z(7z^2 - 3z + 2)$

8. $-6k(3k^3 - 2k - 7)$

9. $-p^2(-3p^2 + 2p - 6)$

In Exercises 10 and 11, translate the verbal phrase to a variable expression. Then simplify.

10. The product of a number, n, and three less than that number.

11. The square of a number, x, times the sum of twice the number and five.

In Exercises 12–15, use the figure at the right.

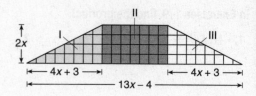

12. Write an expression for the area of each region.

13. Use the result of Exercise 10 to write an expression
    for the area of the entire region.

14. Use the formula for the area of a trapezoid to write
    an expression for the area of the entire region.

15. Compare the expressions obtained in Exercises 13 and 14.

In Exercises 16–19, use the prism at the right.

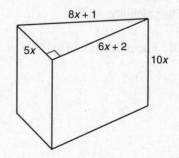

16. Write an expression for the area of the base.

17. Write an expression for the volume of the prism.

18. Write an expression for the surface area of the prism.

19. Evaluate your expressions for the volume and surface
    area when $x = 3$ cm.

1. Describe and correct the error.

$$\cancel{(3x + 5)(2x + 4)} = (3x + 5)(2x) + (5)(2x + 4)$$
$$= 6x^2 + 10x + 10x + 20$$
$$= 6x^2 + 20x + 20$$

In Exercises 2–4, multiply the binomials using a vertical format. Then check the result by using a horizontal format.

2. $3x + 9$
   $\underline{4x + 8}$

3. $5x + 9$
   $\underline{4x + 11}$

4. $6x + 10$
   $\underline{7x + 12}$

In Exercises 5–10, find the product.

5. $(x + 2)(5x + 1)$

6. $(3x + 4)(x + 5)$

7. $(2x + 7)(x + 4)$

8. $(4x + 2)(3x + 6)$

9. $(2x + 9)(x + 4)$

10. $(3x + 2)(5x + 3)$

In Exercises 11–13, write the area of the figure as a polynomial in standard form.

11.

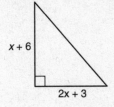

12.

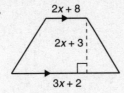

13.

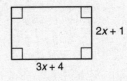

In Exercises 14 and 15 write the area of the shaded region as a polynomial in standard form.

14.

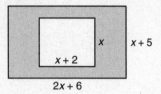

15.

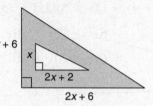

In Exercises 16 and 17, find the area of the mosaic made up of tiles by, first, writing its dimensions and, then, multiplying.

16.

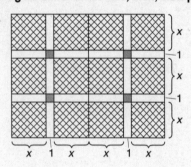

17.

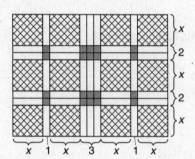

In Exercises 1–4, match the equation with its graph.

A. 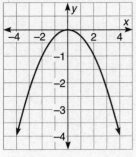   **B.** 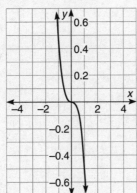   **C.** 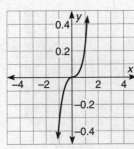   **D.**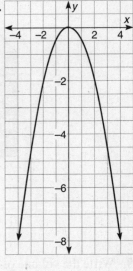

1. $y = \frac{1}{3}x^3$ **2.** $y = -\frac{1}{2}x^2$ **3.** $y = -\frac{1}{2}x^3$ **4.** $y = -\frac{1}{4}x^2$

In Exercises 5–8, make a table of values for the function. Plot the xy-pairs and draw a smooth curve through the points.

5. $y = -2x^2$ **6.** $y = \frac{1}{3}x^2$ **7.** $y = \frac{1}{4}x^3$ **8.** $y = -0.2x^3$

In Exercises 9–13, use the cube shown. All edges of the cube have length of x.

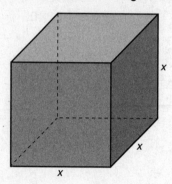

9. Write the volume of the cube as a function of its edge length, x.

10. Find the volume of the cube when the sides are of length 1, 2, 3, and 4. Organize your data in a table.

11. Graph the ordered pairs from your table. Connect the points with a smooth curve.

12. What happens to the volume of a cube if you double the length of its sides?

13. What happens to the volume of a cube if you triple the length of its sides?

Simplify the expression.

1. $\sqrt{49}$

2. $\sqrt{64}$

3. $\sqrt{1600}$

4. $\sqrt{400}$

5. $\sqrt{u^2}$

6. $\sqrt{w^6}$

7. $\sqrt{v^{28}}$

8. $\sqrt{9s^2t^{14}}$

9. $\sqrt{169m^8n^0}$

10. $\sqrt{144q^2r^4s^2}$

11. $\sqrt{d^{16}e^{20}}$

12. $\sqrt{4f^4g^2}$

Solve the equation.

13. $x^2 = 40{,}000$

14. $y^2 = 1600$

15. $c^2 - 5 = 11$

16. $d^2 + 14 = 95$

17. $e^2 + 55 = 64$

18. $3g^2 - 144 = -g^2$

Find the length and width of the rectangle using the given area.

19. Area $= 270 \text{ m}^2$

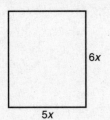

6x

5x

20. Area $= 810 \text{ ft}^2$

2y

5y

Use the Pythagorean theorem to write an equation relating the lengths of the three sides of the right triangle. Solve for the unknown side length.

21.
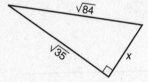

22.
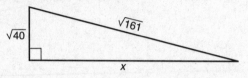

An object is dropped from a building from a height of 100 ft. Its height h (in feet) after t seconds is given by h = –16t² + 100.

23. Find t when $h = 84$.

24. Find t when $h = 0$.

25. What is the significance of the answer in Exercise 24?